My Weekly

2023 ANNUAL

PAGE
88

PAGE
104

PAGE
162

CELEBRITY

FANCY THAT EMPIRES

SWEET TREATS

BRAINBOOSTERS

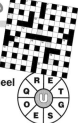

DC Thomson

Kindness And Friendship

Big-hearted celebrities such as Julie Walters lead by example, supporting worthy charities big and small

Supporting Life-Changing Research

Dame Julie Walters lost her grandmother to vascular dementia. "Research offers hope. Hope that one day soon families like mine won't have to witness the devastating effects of dementia," said Julie, while discussing treatment initiatives based on research funded by organisations such as Alzheimer's Research UK. She also backed a petition calling on the government to complete the research funding pledged during an election campaign.

alzheimersresearchuk.org

Listening, Noticing, Talking

Julie supports both national Samaritans charity initiatives and those local to her on the south coast. Of the Brew Monday campaign, which aims to reduce feelings of isolation and loneliness, she says, "I believe we need to listen, notice and talk to people. It isn't a problem to talk about how you are feeling, and things won't get out of control; if anything it will dissipate. It's about not being afraid to approach somebody and noticing what's happening around you."

samaritans.org

Vital Fundraising

"I am absolutely delighted to support and help raise awareness of the lifesaving work of the Midlands Air Ambulance Charity," said Julie, pledging her backing for the service. She was shocked to learn of the £9 million of fundraising required for this vital service, each year. Julie is from the Midlands and trained and worked as a nurse in Birmingham before switching to an acting career.

midlandsairambulance.com ➜

MBE For Matt

Former *Blue Peter, The One Show* and *Countryfile* television presenter – now farmer – Matt Baker was awarded an MBE for his charitable and voluntary services to fundraising in the 2022 New Year's Honours List. This related to several years of sterling work, supporting the annual BBC *Children In Need* fundraising campaign.
bbcchildreninneed.co.uk

Spreading The Love

These celebrities are using their personal platforms to support good causes

Recipe For Life

Nadiya Hussain has been an ambassador for WaterAid since 2016 and in 2021 launched the charity's Thirst for Knowledge appeal for them, helping generations of girls to build a better future by bringing clean water, decent toilets and good hygiene to schools worldwide.

wateraid.org

Sheer(an) Benevolence

Ed Sheeran has a huge career and a huge heart too, notably donating a seven-figure sum to local Suffolk charities during lockdown alone. The Ed Sheeran Suffolk Music Foundation assists Suffolk under-18s with grants to help with the study or playing of music, be it purchasing an instrument or funding studies or rehearsal space. Ed has been made an MBE for his services to charity and music.

essmf.com ➜

Compassion
in the
Community

Offer support or be inspired to set up your own scheme!

Waste Not, Want Not

The SHRUB community cooperative in Edinburgh envisions a world without waste, and aims to empower people to live a low carbon life. "Become a member and learn to fix a bike, swap your preloved things, enjoy some rescued food and be inspired by new ideas," they say. Mindful of the 27 tonnes of food which goes to waste each week in Edinburgh alone, one of SHRUB's activities is the Food Sharing Hub, which offers surplus food from supermarkets and small businesses. shrubcoop.org

Safe Spaces

The Hestia charity provides support for people experiencing domestic abuse or modern slavery and also people with mental health and complex needs. Every year, it helps over 15,000 adults and children in crisis across London and the surrounding regions, aiding them at the time of crisis and also helping them to build a life beyond it. The charity is one of the largest providers of domestic abuse refuges in the capital and the southeast. hestia.org

the Link
visiting scheme

Community Link

The Link Visiting Scheme is a charity operating in Wokingham Borough, with the aim of reducing loneliness and social isolation amongst older people and promoting friendship,improving health, wellbeing and independence. Link Friends are paired up with volunteers for face-to-face befriending, augmented with projects such as Link to Nature

– a seasonal programme of nature-oriented activities such as bulb planting and initiatives encouraging wildlife. They also run a jigsaw exchange and a range of community-based activities. linkvisiting.org

Home Guard

The Wallich charity in Wales has a threefold mission; to provide outreach to people experiencing homelessness with hot food, advice, referrals and pathways out of their situation; supporting people in the immediate and mid term via hostels, emergency night shelters and accommodation for those with specific issues; and creating opportunities via learning and employment projects to help them with their next steps. "Our vision is a Wales where people stand together to provide hope, support and solutions to end homelessness," say The Wallich. thewallich.com ⓂⓌ

JANE CORRY

When One Door Closes

What fresh neighbourly dramas await busybody Patricia in her new home?

Patricia looked round her new apartment with mixed feelings. It was nice enough, with its tall ceilings and lovely view over the park.

Yet something was missing.

If I was in my old home, she thought, someone would be knocking on the door asking if I'd like to go to the village hall coffee morning. Or at least they used to before it all went wrong.

Perhaps she shouldn't have listened to her daughter. Sandy meant well but had this irritating habit of assuming that she was older and wiser than her mother.

"You can't live on your own any more," she'd insisted after Patricia had had that last fall. (She'd been standing on a chair to look out of the window at her neighbour putting a body in his dustbin. She had lost her balance while getting out her mobile to ring the police.)

Patricia felt a feeling of dread.

"If you're asking me to move in with you, that's very kind but I don't think…"

"No, Mum," butted in Sandy. "We both know that wouldn't work."

Phew! Much as she loved her daughter (and Patricia knew the feeling was mutual), they had never rubbed along very easily. Their relationship had definitely got worse after it turned out that the neighbour had been throwing away old clothes and not a body. Even her friends thought she'd gone too far.

"But I've got another idea," Sandy had said. "I've seen a perfect conversion in a lovely old house near me. It will give you independence and I can drop in every now and then. A new start!"

Maybe that might be a good thing, Patricia told herself. Things definitely hadn't been the same since the police had given her a strong verbal warning. (Her "stories", as Sandy pointed out, were always getting her into trouble.)

It's not my fault, Patricia wanted to say. I've always had a vivid imagination ever since…

But what was that? It sounded like a herd of elephants stampeding on the other side of the wall. And what a screeching! Patricia put her hands to her ears. Call that music?

Then the drums started. Oh no!

Patricia had presumed that these apartments were too traditional – and expensive – for young people. But that's the kind of music they played nowadays. Grunge, she believed it was called. She liked to keep up with the times. ➡

ILLUSTRATIONS: MANDY DIXON

She had to do something! It wasn't being nosy, she told herself. It was what anyone would do. Wasn't it?

"Excuse me," she said, knocking on the door. "Do you mind turning down the volume?"

A boy with green and red hair stared at her as if she was some kind of alien.

"We're practising," he said.

Behind him she could see other young men, all with brightly coloured hair and guitars.

"Can you practise somewhere else?" she asked.

"I'm afraid not. Sorry. We've got to keep going now. See you around."

Then he shut the door in her face. How rude!

Patricia tried to ignore the noise. Surely it couldn't go on for that long? Didn't these boys have jobs?

The weeks went by and the music next door continued. She had to go out for a walk to get away from it. The park opposite was busy but no one said hello. So she headed for the fantasy section of the local library to distract herself. It happened to be next to another section which she found equally riveting…

"How are you getting on, Mum?" asked Sandy in her weekly phone call from whichever city she was working in. (Sandy had an important job which Patricia tried to understand but couldn't.)

"The people next door play very loud music," she said.

"Sure you're not exaggerating again?"

"Quite sure." But she could tell her daughter didn't believe her.

So she called one of her old friends from the village; one of the few who was still talking to her.

George was gratifyingly appalled.

"You need to go round again and tell them it's not on. I said it was a bad idea moving away."

It was nice to know someone missed her. Indeed, George had made it clear on several occasions that he would have been happy to have hobbled off into the sunset of old age with her. But, as they say, once burned, twice shy.

"I'm worried about being getting into trouble again," she said.

"Nonsense. You're perfectly justified in complaining."

"You're right, she said firmly. "I'll go round in the morning."

When she woke – with the sun streaming through her windows – her first thought was that there was no music. That was odd. It usually started at this time. All day she kept an ear open, but there was nothing. Yet instead of feeling relieved, she missed hearing something. Anything! The flat was far too quiet.

"I can't live here any more," Patricia said out loud. "I'll go mad with boredom!"

That night, there was still no music. Maybe the lads had gone away. But that flash car was still outside. How could they afford it? Those boys were clearly out of work or else they'd be doing proper jobs instead of playing music all day.

The following day, Patricia woke to hear a banging noise on the other side of the wall. Then there was a definite groan!

Patricia's hair stood on end, the way it had when she'd seen her neighbour carrying out the "body". What if someone was hurt? Taking her umbrella and door keys for protection (both could be used as weapons according to the senior self-protection course she'd taken recently) she gingerly went round to the flat next door. No one answered despite ringing several times. So, taking a deep breath, she tried the door handle. It opened!

Oh my goodness! There'd been a burglary! There were upturned chairs and dirty plates on the floor. The curtains were still closed and there was an awful smell of stale air which reminded her of a time in the Kings Road years ago when she and the girls had…

"Is someone there?" groaned a voice.

Patricia gasped. It was the young man who'd been so rude. He lay on the floor, a guitar cable twisted round his ankle.

before. They'd said she was fantasising. Sometimes she couldn't believe it herself.

"Is there anyone I should call?" she asked while they waited. "Your parents perhaps?"

"They're abroad," he groaned.

"What about the boys who were here?"

"They're away too. I was meant to be joining them today. Can you ring my sister, please?"

He gave her the number just as the ambulance turned up. There wasn't time to write it down but she remembered it.

"Thank you so much," said the sister at the other end. "Which hospital did you say they'd taken him to?"

Luckily Patricia remembered that as well. George used to say she had the sharpest mind in the village and that it

Her eye fell on the microphone in the corner. Unable to resist, she plugged it in

"I tripped over it and haven't been able to move for hours," he said. "I think I hit my head and passed out too. "

The poor boy was clearly in a lot of pain. It took Patricia back to the agony she'd felt – and the embarrassment – after falling off the chair during her "neighbourhood watch".

"I couldn't even reach my mobile," he sobbed. "I thought I was going to die until I heard you coming in."

"It's all right," she said, taking her own mobile out of her pocket (she'd treated herself to a rather flash design to replace the easy-to-use one her daughter had given her.) "I'll call an ambulance. What's your name, by the way?"

"Donny," he groaned.

"Really? I used to know a Donny…"

She stopped. That wasn't important now. Besides, no one had believed her

was a shame no one else recognised it.

"The others are just jealous," he said.

Meanwhile, Patricia stared at the mess around her. She might as well tidy up. It wasn't as if she had anything else to do.

It took her until the evening to do a proper job. For the first time in ages, she'd actually felt useful!

Then her eye fell on the microphone in the corner. Unable to resist, she plugged it in. Closing her eyes, she began to sway. As if by magic, she heard the old words and familiar tunes coming out as if it was twenty-two-year-old Patty singing, not Patricia with her bus pass and pension…

Then there was the sound of a key in the lock. "Hello?"

It was a rather pretty girl who looked a bit like the young man next to her.

"Are we in the right flat, Donny?" ➡

asked the girl, puzzled. "It looks different."

Oh dear. Was she going to accuse her of interfering, like everyone in the village?

"I gave it a quick tidy up," she replied apologetically. "I hope you don't mind but I thought it might help."

"Wow! It looks cool," said Donny. His right leg was in plaster and he was leaning on a crutch. "Thanks so much. You've got a great singing voice, by the way!"

He sounded much politer than when they'd first met!

"My brother said you'd complained about the noise," said the sister. "So I've given him a stern talking to."

"That's all right," said Patricia feeling embarrassed.

"No, it's not. They need to find somewhere else to practise – especially now they've been signed up."

the lead singer in…" She named a group which clearly meant something to them as their eyes widened.

"That rings a bell!" said Donny. "I think our parents had some of your records. I used to play everything in their collection when I was young!"

"Really?" Patricia felt herself redden. "We did quite well for a bit – we were even on Top Of The Pops – but then one of the girls got pregnant and the band drifted apart. It was great while it lasted."

"Wow!" said the sister.

Donny was already on his phone. "I'm Googling you. You were really big!"

Patricia flushed. "It was a long time ago but we had a lot of fun. In fact, we hung out with bands like…"

She then reeled off a list of names which were still going strong.

This young man was interested in her!
It gave her a lovely warm feeling

"Really!" Patricia felt a buzz of déjà vu excitement shooting through her. "How wonderful!"

Donny looked bashful.

"Yeah. We've been trying to make it for years but now it's all beginning to happen. That's why the others have gone off to Florida. I'm meant to be joining them. It's like a dream come true."

Patricia knew all about that! At least until life had changed…

His sister was patting his arm.

"You can still get there in time, Donny. The producer said so."

"You know," said Patricia, suddenly feeling very shy, "I used to be in a band."

"You were?"

They both looked at her as though she'd said something extraordinary.

"My name was Patty then, and I was

"You knew them all?" gasped the sister, her eyes widening.

"I collect their vinyl records," said Donny excitedly. "They're legends!"

Patricia found herself getting rather excited. She'd once told a couple of people in the village about her past but they had looked at her in disbelief. Of course, she'd gone by a stage name then. Even her daughter Sandy (named after a singer friend of hers) didn't like talking about it. That's why it had been so gratifying to find a book that mentioned her and the old band in the Golden Oldie Celebrity section of the library.

"In fact," added Patricia, thinking of the special box she'd started to unpack on the day Donny had his accident, "I've got several photos I took from when we were all together."

"That's amazing!" said Donny. "May I see them?"

"I'd like to as well," said the sister. "But I think we ought to get you to bed."

For a minute, Patricia thought they were talking about her. She did feel a bit tired.

"But I'd like to hear all your stories," protested Donny.

This young man was interested in her! It gave her a lovely warm feeling.

"I'll come back tomorrow," promised Patricia. Then, in case they thought she was being too pushy, she added, "Only if you want me to."

"Of course we do," they chorused.

In fact, she came back every day to help the sister (who was called Ada after her grandmother who had left them the flat) look after Donny.

"I had hangovers too," she said after Donny confessed he'd fallen over the cable because he'd been drinking too much. "But it was just a stage. You'll learn that. I remember once when…" And off she went again. But no one seemed to mind. In fact, they hung on her words!

What a good thing she'd moved! Life was so much more interesting! And she wasn't lonely any more!

"How are you getting on?" asked George when he rang for a chat.

"Wonderful," she said, before telling him what had happened.

"About time someone believed you, lass," he said. "I always did, you know."

Her daughter wasn't so impressed.

"You broke into your neighbour's flat? You could have got into trouble again."

"Actually the door was open and he was grateful for my help."

She had to make allowances for Sandy, Patricia told herself. In those days, unmarried mothers were frowned on. Life had been tough with all the various jobs she'd had to take when it was just the two of them. Much as she loved her daughter, she found herself lapsing into fantasy worlds where she imagined what might have been if the band had continued. Occasionally, this crossed over into real life where she imagined people doing things like putting bodies into dustbins.

Maybe it was because she'd been bored after retirement. But now, spending time with Donny and his sister was giving her a new lease of life.

"I work for a literary agent," said Ada one day. "She wondered if you'd like to write a story about your life?"

"That would be wonderful!"

"The only thing is, we've got a bit of a problem about Donny and I wondered if I could ask you an enormous favour…"

Wow! Patricia couldn't wait to tell her daughter… "Don't worry if you can't get hold of me for a bit. I'm going to accompany my new neighbour to Florida while he records his new album!"

"Is this another story?" asked Sandy.

"Of course not. He even wants me to be a backing singer for one of his songs."

"That's nice, Mum."

Sandy didn't believe her. But that didn't matter, thought Patsy (goodbye Patricia!) as she packed her bags.

Thank goodness she'd broken into Danny's apartment. As they say, thought Patsy happily, when one door closes in life, another opens! **MW**

Turn overleaf for our Author Interview

I'm Fascinated By Complex Families

Sunday Times best-selling author Jane Corry shares her inspiration and the events that have shaped her

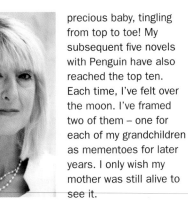

HOW DID YOU FEEL WHEN YOUR FIRST NOVEL WAS ACCEPTED?
Disbelief! I was actually vacuuming the sitting room carpet when the phone rang. It was my then-agent, telling me that a big publisher had made an offer for a romance which I'd written. I'd been trying to get published for ten years and I'd always thought I'd jump in the air for joy when it happened. In fact, it all felt very unreal – especially as my first marriage was breaking up at the same time.

Later, I started writing psychological suspense. When my first novel in that genre was accepted (*My Husband's Wife*), my reaction was utter excitement!

WHAT HAS YOUR PROUDEST MOMENT BEEN?
Getting into the top ten of The Sunday Times with *My Husband's Wife*. Publishers receive sales figures in the middle of the previous week. So I knew in advance but couldn't tell anyone apart from my nearest and dearest. I carried the news in my arms like a precious baby, tingling from top to toe! My subsequent five novels with Penguin have also reached the top ten. Each time, I've felt over the moon. I've framed two of them – one for each of my grandchildren as mementoes for later years. I only wish my mother was still alive to see it.

WHERE DO YOU WRITE?
Three years after my divorce, I married again. We moved to the south-west. My study is on the top floor and you can just about glimpse the sea. The walls are lined with books. I have a lavender bag on one side of my screen and a a photograph of my great-grandfather looking down on me. He was called Frank Romer and was a doctor and a published novelist (Duckworth and Collins). My dog sleeps behind me on a sofa which I am constantly vacuuming because of his hairs! When my grandchildren come round, they love racing up to my study and printing out pictures to colour in! There's also a wooden wall hanging which says *By the sea, all worries wash away.*

WHAT INSPIRES YOU?

Families! I'm fascinated by complicated relationships. Many of us want to be part of a warm, loving family but it isn't easy because we all have different views! After my first marriage ended, I took a job as a writer in residence of a high-security male prison for three years. On certain occasions, I met the families when they visited. Many were shocked that their loved ones had committed crimes. I like to explore how families can get caught up in breaking the law, sometimes without meaning to. My new book *We All Have Our Secrets* is about two women who do just that.

AN ACT OF LOVING KINDNESS

My mother was one of the kindest people I've ever known. She lost her mother at the age of nine to cancer during the war, which made her very sympathetic to others. So my sister and I grew up with the same attitude. I often give advice to people who want to get published and I also funded a writer in residence for a year at the prison where I used to work. Writing can help people rethink what they've done in the past and forge a better future. Talking can also be a great act of loving kindness. One of my friends rang me every day for months after my first marriage ended. She is now going through a hard time herself so it's my turn to return the favour. Readers might also be interested in a short story collection, called *Everyday Kindness*, edited by L J Ross. Each tale is about kindness and has been written free of charge, by contributing authors including myself. All proceeds go to Shelter.

MY FAVOURITE VIEW

This has to be the sea! Every day, throughout the year, I cycle down at 7.30am with an artist friend. We swim across the bay in our wetsuits. If the sea is too rough, we walk along the promenade instead. Either way, the view is amazing. It is the same and yet different! The tide might be out or in. Sometimes the cliff formation is different because of all-too-frequent landslides. But it's the colours which take your breath away! The line between the sea and the sky sometimes looks like a Monet painting with soft blues and pinks. At other times, it looks as though the sky is on fire. I never tire of looking at it, which is why the sea always comes into my novels. **MW**

Jane Corry's new novel is called WE ALL HAVE OUR SECRETS and is published by Penguin.

You Are Invited…

Catering for the whole family at Christmas is chaotic and exhausting – but could she really give it all up?

By Teresa Ashby

B ad news," Ross grimaces as he puts his phone back in his pocket. "Oh, dear, isn't your mum coming for Christmas?"

"Yes, but she wants to bring her friends, Joyce and Elaine."

My heart sinks.

"She says to remind you that Joyce can't tolerate sprouts, and Elaine has a problem with Christmas pudding, so if you could do broccoli and perhaps some gateau…" His voice withers away.

I used to love Christmas, no matter how many people turned up. It was fun putting two tables together and using folding and garden chairs to fit everyone in, but in recent years it's become just hard work.

I've already had a phone call from my mum reminding me that Dad doesn't like turkey, and to say she hoped my mother-in-law wasn't bringing any of her weird friends with her.

Don't get me started on my kids. They were far less fussy when they were little, and the older ones' partners aren't much better. There are two vegans among them, which isn't a problem as I make a mean nut roast, but then there's sixteen year old Michael who doesn't like meat *or* vegetables. He's a challenge I can tell you! Last year all he had on his plate was

a giant Yorkshire pudding and a blob of bread sauce!

Gone are the days when I'd just load up all the plates and everyone would tuck in and leave what they didn't want.

I blame my dad. A few years ago he said he didn't actually like turkey, and if it wasn't too much trouble, could I do him a little beef joint – which I was quite happy to do.

However, it opened the floodgates to a whole raft of special requests. So there's so much to remember these days. I've written two pages of instructions for myself so I don't forget to put anything on or take anything off.

It's going to be like playing Tetris trying to fit everything in the oven.

"I can't do it, Ross!" I burst out. "I'm forty-five! Life is meant to be getting easier not harder!"

"I'll help," he says. "You just tell me what to do."

I show him my notes and he goes pale.

"Book us into a hotel," I say. "I'm not doing Christmas this year. That will surprise them!"

I 'm worn out on Christmas Eve. I've been hard at it all day. The vegetables and meat are prepared. It's just a matter of putting everything in the oven at the right time, but someone else will have to do it this year. ➡

We sneak out of the house during the evening and head for the hotel down the road where we're greeted with mulled wine and dinky little mince pies.

"This is the life," I say.

There is music and dancing and we stay up late, but not as late as we would at home. I wonder if anyone has noticed we're missing.

We've left our phones behind. Nothing is going to spoil Christmas!

In the morning, we go down to the hotel dining room for breakfast.

"I hope they remember to put the meat in on time," I say.

I miss the chat. I miss Mum talking about Christmas when I was little. And I

He sighs wistfully, then puts his cup down with a clatter.

The four course Christmas dinner at the hotel had sounded lovely, but I long for my own kitchen.

Everyone looks at us as if we're mad when we check out.

All our guests have arrived when we get home. Our offspring have set out and laid the two tables and are busy chopping vegetables and mixing pudding batter. Someone has already put the turkey in the oven.

"Happy Christmas," Mum says, giving us both a hug. "Did you have a nice walk?"

Our kids hug us and Michael says he

Christmas dinner at the hotel sounded lovely but I long for my own kitchen

miss my kids updating us on what they've been up to.

I look at Ross. He pours another coffee. "Quiet isn't it?" he says.

"Too quiet?" I ask.

He shrugs.

"Do you reckon your mum's opened the wine yet?" I say and he laughs.

She usually opens a bottle when I start cooking and my glass never empties, so by the time I dish up, I'm singing Christmas songs.

Last year I got in a muddle and put the wrong stuff on the plates, but no one minded.

There had been much laughter as everyone swapped this and that.

"Do you remember last year…?" we say in unison.

"Never again," Ross says and he blinks as if the thought upsets him.

"What do you suppose they're doing now?" I bite my lip.

thought we were having a lie-in! I realise I've never given them the chance to help out before. Christmas dinner was always my thing!

Ross's mum puts a glass of wine in my hand before you can say Rudolf.

My eldest daughter Gemma whispers in my ear, "Next year, there'll be another one joining us."

"Good," I say. There's always been room at our table for more.

Then she adds a word that makes my heart soar. "Granny!"

I start singing early. I can't help myself. Best Christmas surprise ever! (MW)

MY INSPIRATION

I find inspiration everywhere around me – from my family and pets to a walk on the beach or even a few overheard words. What I love is how it strikes without warning!

◆ Foul-smelling barbarians? Not a bit of it! Vikings bathed at least once a week – far more often than other Europeans of their day.

◆ Theories suggest that the local women married the invading Vikings because they were much cleaner and better looking than the local men!

◆ Vikings were active in the slave trade, selling Anglo-Saxon, Celtic and Slavic young men and women captured in their raids...

◆ ... and yet Viking women enjoyed more rights than most of their time – they could inherit property, divorce and reclaim their dowries.

◆ Most Viking men wielded scythes, not swords! For the best part of the year, most peacefully farmed crops and raised livestock to feed their families.

◆ One of the Viking gods was Ullr – the god of skiing. Vikings not only travelled more efficiently on skis but skiing was a form of recreation too.

FANCY THAT!

Fascinating facts on
The Valiant Vikings!

◆ To conform to their culture's beauty standards, dark-haired Vikings (mostly men) washed their hair (and beards) with high lye content soap to bleach it – which also meant they did not have lice!

◆ Vikings did not call themselves Vikings – they were a large group of diverse tribes across the land that now makes up Denmark, Norway and Sweden.

◆ A Viking was also the first to discover Greenland – Erik the Red founded the first settlement there.

◆ Vikings did not wear horned hats – painters seem to have fabricated the trend in the 19th century, inspired by Roman chroniclers who wrote of the ceremonial horned hats of the Norse priests.

◆ Vikings travelled as far as Baghdad and North America and their descendants can be found across the whole of Europe.

◆ Tuesday (Tyr), Wednesday (Oden), Thursday (Thor), and Friday (Freya) are all named after Norse gods.

◆ However, they did bury their dead warriors in their boats, surrounded by their worldly goods – it was believed they would need it all in the afterlife.

Viking excavation dig sites have turned up tweezers, razors, combs and ear cleaners

Stocking Up!

Follow Larry and Jo – if you can – as they brave the crowds with a list and an ambitious timetable

By Steve Beresford

Crikey, it was crowded. Maybe stopping for a short break wasn't such a good idea. The café was fairly heaving and it might have been wise to snag a table before they queued for their refreshments.

"Quick!" Larry nodded towards a table, unable to point with the loaded tray in his hands. Two shopping bags hung from one hand too and he wore a packed rucksack. Talk about overloaded. "There's one, just coming free." An elderly couple were getting up from their seats, gathering their things, clearly vacating the corner table in Harland's café.

Jo was off like a sprinter when the starter pistol fires, dodging between the packed tables, heavy bags swinging in her hands, casting brief apologies to those she banged on the way. She made it just before a family of five arrived.

"Sorry!" She dumped her bags on one chair and flopped on to an opposite one. "This table's taken!"

This was greeted by a chorus of disappointment from the children of the family and some very un-festive barbed muttering from the parents. Jo smiled in return, feeling her cheeks redden under the harsh glares. She felt a tiny twinge of guilt, but in this sort of crush… every man for himself. Or woman, obviously, in this case.

"Good one, Jo." Larry arrived with the tray of coffee and buns. Jo moved the used teapot and cups out of the way and then took the tray off Larry to set it down on the table. He swung his bags on to the other seat, shrugged off the rucksack, then flopped down, puffing out a long breath, already exhausted.

"Can you believe what this is like?" He gestured around the cafe. "It's bedlam."

"We should have expected it would be fairly crowded," Jo said. "But I never thought it would be this bad." She now took the time to rearrange her own carriers, propping two against her legs beneath the table and placing her special shopping bag on the empty seat next to her. She flexed her aching fingers and inspected her palms, with were criss-crossed with angry red lines. "Those handles really dig in."

"It's that trendy bag you've got." Larry said. "All style, no comfort. You should have stuck with these." He jerked a thumb at his own bags with their soft linen handles. "Although my back's starting to go funny." He rolled his shoulders. "I'm not convinced the rucksack was such a good idea. I keep turning round and knocking people over."

Jo took a bite of her bun, then thumbed up her Christmas shopping checklist on the screen of her phone. She scrolled down it, assessing her progress. It was a big list with lots of names and lots of presents. However, some presents had turned out to be more difficult to find than others.

"What did we eventually get for Ann?"

Jo had typed in 'make-up set' next to Ann's name, but the shop had sold out of the set Jo had particularly wanted to buy. Now, with all the bustle and confusion she couldn't remember what she'd got instead.

"Golfing socks." Larry's mumbled reply emerged through a mouthful of cream bun. Crumbs sprayed. "Sorry."

"Socks?" Jo didn't remember that. "We didn't get socks, did we?"

"I did," Larry said. "I got them while you were messing about by the handbags."

Jo frowned. "Socks for Auntie Ann?"

"For Ann? No, for Dan!" Larry chuckled, spraying more crumbs. "I thought you said Dan." He swiped the crumbs away again, minus the apology. "It's all the noise."

There was a lot of noise. Everyone was trying to talk over everyone else. Babies were crying. Children were screaming. Parents were shouting.

"You got that collection of miniature perfumes for Ann," he said.

"Right! Of course!" Jo remembered now: the woman behind her in the queue shouting into her phone, the haughty assistant, the problem with the dodgy barcode, the card reader that didn't work when she tapped her card against it, the receipt that ripped as it came out of the till. It had been one of the more traumatic purchases she'd made that day. It was no wonder she'd momentarily blotted it out. She typed an amendment to her ➙

checklist. Then she realised something. "Hold on, Dan's name isn't on my list."

"No, I know." Larry grinned. "I just thought I'd get his golfing socks while I was there." He took a swig of his coffee. "You don't mind, do you?"

"I suppose not," Jo said. "It didn't upset the schedule. But no more unauthorised purchases or my system will fall apart."

Larry saluted. "Aye, captain."

Jo scrolled up and down her checklist, inserting ticks here and there.

Little Adam, their lovable nephew – jigsaw – check. Her brother Peter – luxury spanner set – check. Larry's sister Carole – handbag – check. Alice – novelty corkscrew – check. Alice did like her wine.

Other names received ticks too.

oven gloves for Granny Maggie." Granny Maggie spent most of her life in the kitchen, cooking and baking and creating. "You know what she likes. Countrified. Floral. That sort of thing. Farm animals might be good, for a change."

"Farm animals." Larry nodded. "Right-oh. You can count on me."

"I doubt that."

"Charming."

Jo smiled to show she was only teasing. "I'll meet you by the fountain in Centenary Square in exactly twenty-five minutes."

"Should we synchronise our watches?"

"What?"

"Well, you're making it sound like a military operation. We're doing our Christmas shopping. It's meant to be fun."

Larry set off purposefully. Within seconds he was gone, swallowed up

They'd done well so far, especially in here. Harland's was a proper old-fashioned department store, with plenty of choice. There weren't many places like this left.

"So far so good," Jo said. "I reckon we're well over halfway."

"Only halfway?" Larry said. He leaned forward to peer at her list, as though he didn't believe her. "My feet are killing me."

"Your feet?" Jo said. "What about mine? I had the female equivalent of King Kong trample all over them while I was getting Carole's handbag. It was like a herd of wildebeest stampeding in size nines. And she didn't even say sorry."

"I reckon you need full body armour to survive unscathed in these conditions." Larry swigged the rest of his coffee and set the cup back on the saucer. "Where next?"

"Bookshop." Jo had a plan. "That's where I'm going anyway. You're going to…" She referred to her checklist. "…to Marwells to get a new apron and a pair of

"Fun? Fun doesn't come into it," Jo said. "Now hurry up, or we won't get everything before the shops close."

"Yes, ma'am!" Larry saluted again – a joke that had already worn thin.

Jo reached down to gather the bags around her feet. Another family spotted the movement and immediately homed in to take over the table.

Larry took his share of the bags, pulled on his rucksack, pecked her cheek and set off, striding purposefully into the swarm of people surrounding the café. Within seconds he was gone, swallowed up completely.

Jo turned and set off in the opposite direction, heading for the other door that went out into Beacon Street.

She tried to keep to a steady pace, but too many people were rushing around and she got caught up in the flow. The funny thing was, the faster her feet moved, the less distance she seemed to travel in a straight line.

So it was all a bit hectic. So she was tired and her feet hurt. So the noise was making her ears sing. But by the end of the day she would have all her Christmas presents. Not like some people: buying one present here and one there, a bit of shopping one day and a bit some other day, being disorganised and forgetting someone important because they hadn't made a list.

No, Jo was organised. She knew exactly where she was going, what she was going to buy when she got there and how much she was prepared to spend on each individual item. Barring the odd hiccup – such as Auntie Ann's sold-out make-up set – it made for surprisingly easy, hassle-free shopping.

Well, hassle-free had it not been for the crowds. But then, she admitted to herself, at this time of year crowds were unavoidable.

Horns tooted. Engines revved. Music played from different shops, creating a mumbled cacophony of half-recognised festive tunes. And people were shouting even more loudly than they were inside. It felt as if the entire local population, and then some, had descended on the town centre. Elbows became lethal weapons, guided with precision into unsuspecting ribs. Jo's elbows, however, had quickly become powerless, weighed down with heavy bags.

The blizzard-like snow wasn't helping. It was treacherously slushy underfoot and without an empty third hand her compact umbrella lay uselessly in her handbag.

Snow was very nice for Christmas. Very festive. But she'd had enough now. Flakes hit her eyes and melted in her ears. Her scarf protected her neck, but there was nothing to protect her hair, which was now – she glimpsed her reflection in a – damp

and frizzy. Her aching feet were soaked.

She made it to the bookshop, whizzed from shelf to shelf over the two floors, then stood in line to pay. Forty minutes later she staggered up to Larry by the fountain.

He made a big thing of looking at his watch. "Twenty-five minutes, you said."

"Don't start. There was a huge queue."

"There's a surprise." He held out a hand. "Here, let me have that."

She passed on the big hessian bag from the bookshop. Larry almost stumbled over when he took the weight.

"What have you bought? The full works of Agatha Christie? In hardback?"

"There are some good bargains in there."

"I hope so. Lucky you've got a sturdy bag." He rearranged his bags, swapping from hand to hand until satisfied the weight was evenly distributed. "Where next then?"

"To get some saucepans." Jo started walking again. "They're for..."

"...for Sarah," Larry said, hurrying to keep up. "See I do listen. Sometimes." He grinned. "Your hair looks nice."

"Thank you!"

"The Bride of Frankenstein look is very trendy at the moment. I did tell you to get a jacket with a hood."

"So you did." But Jo wasn't going to be sidetracked. "Still, not much left to get now."

"Then we just have to wrap them..."

"But at least we've got all next year to do that." Jo was feeling pleased with herself. "You know, I can't understand why so many people leave it to the last moment to do their Christmas shopping. Everything is so much cheaper in the Boxing Day sales." Ⓜ

MY INSPIRATION

I'm inspired to write because I love stories. They're a kind of magic, allowing us to experience lives other than our own, sometimes beyond even our own imagination.

Make A Wish

If resolutions were wishes, how would you hope to bring in the New Year? Carrie knows exactly how she would!

By Rosemary Hayes

Hi George, here's some pizza and movies for us to ring in the New Year," I said, when George opened the door to his apartment.

"Ah, Carrie, you are sweet, but you should be out at some party having fun, meeting someone, not stuck here with me. How else will you find a boyfriend?"

I put the pizza on the coffee table. George was like a protective grandfather and more intent on finding me a boyfriend than I was. "I'm not unhappy being an unattached woman. But if New Year came with wishes instead of resolutions I might wish to meet someone special."

"Someone like my grandson Philip?" George winked. "I've noticed the look on your face when you stare at the photo of him on the shelf."

It seemed I was sprung. Philip was thirty, single, had a successful graphic design business… and the photo showed

couldn't help notice that his photo didn't do his smile justice at all.

"Hiya Phil," said George. "What are you doing here? Didn't you have a New Year Party to go to?"

"I didn't want you to be alone on New Year's Eve. But I see you aren't alone."

"No, Carrie insisted on spending the evening with me instead of going to a party herself. Isn't she a gem?"

"She sure is."

I could say the same about Philip He was taller than his photo suggested, and it sure didn't capture the blue of his eyes. Or the warmth that shone there.

"Sit down, sit," said George. He was on the single armchair which left the two seater for Philip and I to share. I was more than aware of how close he was to me. I didn't mind at all. He put his pizza on the coffee table next to mine.

"Eat up you two," said George, standing. "Excuse me for a sec while I make an important phone call."

I couldn't help but notice that his photo didn't do his smile justice at all

a smile that made my pulse jump. Sadly George's grandson lived far away.

Just then I heard a man's voice from the direction of the front door. "Hi Grandad."

It took a moment for me to register that it wasn't just any man in the room. It was Philip. I hadn't heard a knock on the door. He must have his own key. When he smiled at me, with surprise in his eyes, I

After George walked down the short hallway and went through a doorway on the left Philip opened the pizza box and offered me some first.

"Thank you." I picked up a slice. The cheese stretched in long lines. "Mmmm, cheesy."

"Me or the pizza?" Phil looked so adorably doubtful I had to smile.

"The pizza," I smiled. It was a ➡

comfortable silence as we ate pizza. In between mouthfuls I said, "I was surprised to see you here. Don't you live several hours from here?"

"I've just moved back. I've been worried about Granddad since Grandma passed away."

Family was important to me. It warmed my heart to know it was important to Philip too.

"I'm glad you're here," he added. "It gives me a chance to say thank you for helping him out so much. I really appreciate it. Granddad has spoken about you a lot, you know, every time I called to check on him."

"Has he? All good I hope?"

"All very complimentary. And having met you now, I totally agree."

I'd never been good at responding to compliments so I could feel my cheeks grow warm.

"Only a little, but I'll forgive you."

George finally reappeared. "You two getting along OK?"

"More than OK, I think." Philip said, looking at me.

"No argument here," I said. "It's about time you came back though, George. The pizza's getting cold."

The rest of the evening was non-stop

"Granddad has spoken about you a lot, every time I called to check on him"

"Thanks." I pointed down the hallway. "George sure is taking his time on that phone call."

"Which is pretty strange," Phil said, "Considering his mobile phone is sitting on the side table right there. I think someone might be playing matchmaker. I kind of guessed when he said, 'I have to make an important phone call'. He's a wonderful grandfather, but a terrible actor. Mind you," his lovely blue eyes held mine. "I don't mind him playing cupid at all, as long as he doesn't come out of his bedroom wearing wings."

I couldn't help but laugh. I liked Philip's sense of humour.

"Did you know your eyes sparkle when you laugh?" said Phil "Uh oh, that sounds cheesy, doesn't it?"

conversation but as midnight approached George fell asleep in his sofa chair. Only Phil and I were awake, the space between us slowly shrinking as midnight approached. Then midnight struck.

"Happy New Year," I said.

"Happy New Year," said Phil.

He leant in close and kissed me. There were fireworks. Definitely fireworks. It seemed my New Year wish had come true after all. Ⓜ

MY INSPIRATION

My family is my inspiration: my husband, children, grandchildren. They are my reason for getting up in the morning. They are my world and always will be!

148
Calories
per 25g

Spiced Nuts

Ingredients (Makes 550g)

- **2tbsp Worcestershire sauce**
- **1tsp chilli powder**
- **2tbsp olive oil**
- **1tsp sea salt flakes**
- **½tsp paprika**
- **1tsp caster sugar**
- **500g mixed nuts**
  eg cashews, almonds,
  pecans, walnuts and
  pistachios

1 Preheat the oven to 180°C/Fan 160°C/ Gas 4. Combine the Worcestershire sauce, chilli powder, olive oil, sea salt, paprika and sugar in a large bowl. Add the nuts and stir together.

2 Spread on to a baking sheet lined with non-stick baking paper and bake for 10min, turning after 5min. Transfer to a tray lined with kitchen paper and leave to cool.

3 Store in an airtight container for up to 3 weeks. If giving as a gift, in Cellophane packaging, label with a use-by date of 7 days.

➜ **55**

The Wedding Rehearsal

Amid the chaos of her daughter's winter nuptial preparations, Sarah had a certain glow about her

By Jan Snook

Winter had always been Sarah's favourite season.

In summer she was torn between doing the garden (she could always find something urgent to do there, particularly if the sun was out), and the many indoor chores she'd been putting off. Spring was lovely, but held too many sad memories.

Autumn had a certain charm, she had to admit as she looked out at her own garden, with all its shades of brown and gold, but how she hated raking up leaves! Still, it was October, and winter would soon be here, and there would be Christmas to look forward to, cosy evenings in front of a fire, and generously buttered crumpets. And best of all this year, Eleanor's wedding.

A winter wedding! Thank goodness

The words 'for your age' hovered unspoken in the air.

"And I don't mean 'for your age'," Eleanor amended, clearly aware of what her mother was thinking. "There are plenty of thirty year olds who would like to look as good as you do. You're going to look stunning at the wedding. Just try not to outshine me, please."

Sarah gave a wry smile. There was no danger of that.

Anyway, she was glad that it was almost winter, and that Andrew wouldn't see the bits of herself she didn't like, she thought, her mind turning yet again to the coming weekend. He wouldn't see those bits yet, at all events, a very quiet little voice whispered in her head. Not that she was expecting this first meeting to lead to anything (she was shying away from calling

"You'll look stunning at the wedding. Just try not to outshine me, please"

she wouldn't have to flit about in a floaty summer dress! She had reached that age where she would gaze critically at her upper arms in the mirror, and had concluded that her feet were not as pretty as they had once been either.

"You're mad, you know that, don't you?" her daughter said when Sarah voiced these thoughts. "No-one looks as good as you."

it a date, even to herself)… And anyway, she wasn't even sure that a visit to an art gallery on a Sunday afternoon counted as a date, did it?

Her mind wandered off into yet another daydream about the coming weekend, only snapping out of it when Eleanor spoke.

"What are you going to wear?"

Sarah frowned at her daughter in ➤

surprise, then her brain clicked into gear.

"But you know what I'm going to wear, you came with me. We bought it ages ago."

"Ah, so you do remember that I came over to discuss my wedding then?" Eleanor smiled. "It's just that you looked miles away. Dreaming about a good-looking man and an art gallery I imagine… But I actually meant, what are you going to wear on your date? First date, big decision!"

"I'd hardly call it a date!" Sarah said crossly, aware that she was blushing.

"Well, I don't know what else you'd call it," Eleanor murmured, pulling a wedding magazine out of her bag and flicking idly through it. Then she looked up. "Why don't we decide what you're going to wear on Sunday, and then you might be able to

had been friends with Annie and Andrew since before they'd all been married. Almost twenty-five years ago now. But once Annie had left Andrew for a fitness instructor a decade ago, the friendship had waned, until they weren't doing much more than exchanging Christmas cards.

When her own husband, Henry, had been killed in a skiing accident three years ago, Andrew had come unexpectedly to the funeral. After that there had been a few tentative phone calls on his part, but she had been too lost in grief to show any enthusiasm, and the calls had dwindled.

The invitation to visit the current Kandinsky exhibition had come out of the blue, written on the back of a postcard of a Kandinsky painting of concentric circles.

He had always, she remembered, swept his friends up in his enthusiasm for art

concentrate on the bridesmaids, OK?"

Sarah's head whipped up. Eleanor laughed indulgently.

"Wow, you really are in the middle of an all-out fantasy, aren't you? I meant my bridesmaids, Mum, not yours!"

"I don't know what you're talking about, Andrew's just an old friend," Sarah said unconvincingly, but they both went upstairs to choose an outfit for Sunday.

Sarah arrived at the gallery a little early, and went to the café to have a cup of coffee, sitting where she could see visitors arriving. She saw Andrew making his way to the front entrance a minute or two later, and she was relieved to see that he looked casually smart, so she wouldn't look overdressed beside him.

She finished her coffee quickly and met him in the entrance hall, feeling rather nervous – which was ridiculous, she acknowledged to herself: she and Henry

Andrew kissed her on the cheek in greeting before leading her into the first room of paintings, and Sarah felt herself relax as he started to talk animatedly about the art. He was an architect and had always, she remembered, swept his friends up in his enthusiasm for the visual arts.

Why had she worried? The intervening years simply slipped away as they wandered from room to room, admiring the paintings and catching up on over ten years of news.

"So, little Eleanor's getting married!" he said as they followed the visit to the gallery with a walk along the river. The last of the leaves were falling, and the spiky reflections of the trees broke and reformed as the river rippled in the breeze.

"In December, yes. There's so much to do, I wouldn't have believed it. And of course she's at work all week, and so am I, so most of our Saturdays are taken up with discussing it."

"Tell me about it." Andrew raised his eyebrows. "Both my girls are now married and – well just between us, I think they were afraid that I'd feel left out, so they consulted me about each and every scrap of ribbon, or flower arrangement or what-have-you. There is nothing I don't know about weddings now, so if you need a fully-fledged expert, I'm your man!"

This actually proved to be true, somewhat to Sarah's surprise.

The first 'date' had been followed by visits to the theatre, long country walks (with pub lunches thrown in), and even Christmas shopping expeditions in Andrew's silver-grey Jaguar, which, he confessed, was his pride and joy.

Andrew may have known about weddings, but he was clueless as to what to buy his daughters, sisters and mother for Christmas, Sarah discovered, and she came into her own as chief present chooser.

Andrew, on the other hand, came up with effective solutions to the various problems the wedding was causing, which ranged from caterers letting them down to the exorbitant cost of flowers in December. Not forgetting the little bridesmaid who had grown six inches since Sarah had made her dress.

Eleanor wanted a small wedding, and didn't want to spend a lot of money (or rather, Sarah suspected, didn't want to involve her mother in unnecessary expense), which made things even more difficult. But for every problem Andrew came up with a sensible suggestion, which Sarah would then pass on to Eleanor, until at last Eleanor decided to cut out the middle man (her mother) and simply email Andrew for advice.

One Saturday afternoon in November when Sarah and Andrew were having a cup of tea

at Sarah's house, they heard Eleanor letting herself in.

"It's me," she called out from the hall, "may I come in?"

"Of course you can come in," Sarah said, mildly puzzled.

"Well I thought I'd better ask," Eleanor said breezily, "who knows what you two might be up to?"

Sarah widened her eyes at her daughter warningly, but Eleanor just laughed, and tossed an envelope into Andrew's lap.

"We'd like you to come to the wedding, always assuming Mum hasn't asked anyone else as her plus-one…?"

She didn't give Andrew any time to answer, but continued, "but I'm afraid there are some strings attached…"

Andrew was grinning broadly.

"It's all right, your mum's just been telling me about the wedding car fiasco, and I have a solution. You were only having one car, weren't you? Why don't I put on a chauffeur's cap and take you to church in my Jag? It will look very wedding-y with white ribbon on the front. What do you think?"

He paused. "I haven't offered before because it might have sounded as if I was angling for an invitation to the wedding," he said diffidently, "which I absolutely wasn't expecting, I might add."

Eleanor frowned.

"It's a very kind suggestion… but does a chauffeur's cap go with a morning suit, do you think? And I was sort of hoping you'd be sitting in the back with me…" ➤

Sarah and Andrew were both staring at her.

"I mean, you were my dad's oldest friend, and, well, someone's got to give me away, haven't they?"

Sarah and Andrew both started talking at once, Sarah hugging her daughter and Andrew saying how honoured he would be, but Eleanor cut them short:

"Which means," she added, "that you'll need to come to the wedding rehearsal in a fortnight's time."

the hem of her dress, tearing it, and the best man was twenty minutes late.

"What is it they say?" Andrew asked with a reassuring smile as the wedding party gathered in the pub opposite the church for some lunch when the rehearsal was over, "if the dress rehearsal goes badly, the performance itself will be a roaring success? It'll all be absolutely fine on the day – trust me."

"Well – it was certainly

"If the dress rehearsal goes badly, the performance will be a roaring success"

The next two weeks flew by. The groom's brother was co-opted to drive the Jaguar, the bridesmaid's dress now fitted, the final touches were added to the cake and the orders of service were printed. And Andrew and Sarah still managed to spend a lot of time together.

Sarah was finding it hard to believe how much she had come to rely on him. It was only ten short weeks since he had come back into her life, and she didn't know how on earth she would cope if he left it again. Ten weeks wasn't long in anyone's book. Things could still fall apart all too easily. She went hot and cold at the thought.

But not today, she thought, as Andrew arrived, beaming, to collect her to go to the church for the rehearsal.

The rehearsal though turned out to be a bit of a washout. The vicar was apologetic that everyone was freezing – they only put the heating on for actual services, because of the cost. He was also sorry he'd got to rush off early – he had double-booked himself and had a christening in the next parish in an hour.

The bridesmaid managed to tread on

useful," Eleanor said, pulling a wry face at her fiancé. "At least we know lots of things not to do now!"

"What a disaster!" Sarah whispered later, when the others had left, and she and Andrew were alone once again. "Poor Eleanor."

Andrew laughed.

"It'll all be fine, don't worry. And I thought it was extremely useful, all things considered, didn't you?"

"Yes," Sarah agreed, smiling, "Eleanor found it very useful, and I'm sure next Saturday will go really smoothly now."

"Yes, I'm sure it will," Andrew said, taking Sarah's hand, his eyes twinkling, "but actually I wasn't thinking of Eleanor's wedding. I meant that the experience would come in useful for ours." ⓂⓌ

MY INSPIRATION

I love organising weddings but with both daughters married, I can only plan them in fiction. I so want my characters to be happy that it's hard not to marry them off in paragraph one!

Brain Boosters

Codeword

Each letter of the alphabet has been replaced by a number. The numbers for the first name of our chosen celebrity are given. Complete the puzzle to find out which future co-stars did Olivia Colman meet at Cambridge University Footlights Dramatic Club?

A B C D E F G H I J K L M N O P Q R S T U V W X Y Z

1	2	3	4	5	6	7	8	9 A	10	11	12	13
14	15	16	17 L	18 O	19 I	20	21	22	23	24	25	26 V

Turn To Page 157 For Solutions

22	9 A	26	19 V	22 I		10	19 I	11	4	12	1	17 L	17 L

9 A	25	22		16	18 O	7	1	16	11		3	1	7	7

New Year, New Ways

Annie had always been a little timid – that is, until she took a chance and went to the other side…

By Sheila Blackburn

Annie folded the tea towel and looked round the kitchen. All clean and tidy. She nodded to herself.

Back in the hall, the chairs and tables had been cleared in readiness for sweeping up. Rick was heaping black bin liners by the rear door and Paula was hovering near to the music system, ready to silence the golden oldies CD.

Annie retrieved sweeping brushes from storage behind a thick curtain.

"There we are, then – Christmas done and dusted and the in-between party over for another twelve months," Paula sang out "Next stop, New Year!"

She left her CD post and hurried to give Annie a hand with the sweeping.

"Another good party for the records," she grinned. "Bit of a lift between Christmas and New Year means a lot to the Seniors."

Managing a grin, Annie pointed out that it wouldn't be long before some of the committee would be on the receiving end of the annual treat. "The years come and go so fast, we'll soon qualify for a turkey dinner ourselves!"

Paula gasped. "Now don't you go saying stuff like that!" she warned and shook her brush in mock disbelief. "We're absolutely not ready for paper hats and a tuneless singer yet, you silly thing."

Annie raised her eyebrows. "Well…" And they both burst out laughing.

"Good to see you still have a sense of fun, anyway." Paula leaned on her brush and looked searchingly into Annie's face.

"Meaning?"

Paula spoke gently. "You can't fool me, Annie. You've busied yourself here all day but I can tell there's something bothering you. Look, why don't we call in at Rosie's Café and you can tell me all about it?"

Annie shrugged, wondering what to say. She resumed her brushing quietly, relieved when all was tidy and Rick moved to the door to switch off the lights.

"We're going for a coffee – come and join us," she suggested and was glad when he agreed.

Rick locked up and the threesome stepped into the cold darkness of the late December afternoon. They walked through the car park and onto Church Street. Loud with laughter and bon homie, early evening revellers made their way into the local inn.

At the corner of School Lane, they stopped for a passing car, full of de-mob happy workers, waving streamers with the raucous joy of holiday freedom. Now the shuttered row of shops came into view, their Christmas displays still a cheerful trail of colour. They walked on, passing houses curtained against the night ahead, passed the beautiful, glittering white lights of the Church yard Christmas tree, pulled at party popper streamers tangled in a holly tree and moving gently in a light breeze.

"Here we are." Rick held the café door open and they stepped into candlelight and the smell of cinnamon and hot mice pies.

"My treat," Annie said, waving away any protests as they took a window table. Rosie arrived to take their order and soon they were tucking into brandy-cream topped mince pies and mulled wine.

"Cheers!" Rick raised his glass and clinked it with the others. "We deserve this," he said and took a welcome swig.

Paula watched Annie cutting her mince pie carefully, deep in thought.

"So – how was your Christmas?" she began.

"Just the usual with Mum and Dad," Annie looked wistful. "Yours?"

"Madness – utter chaos as usual. Wouldn't have it any other way… your mum and dad OK?"

Annie sipped her wine and smiled at Paula's clumsy way of broaching the real subject of her concern. "I know you think I'm being a miserable Grinch for the time of year…" she began.

"No." Paula licked brandy cream off her fingers. "But you're not your usual self. It worries me. So I hold my hands up – nosey I may be, but concerned – definitely."

Rick shook his head and ordered a pot of tea and more mince pies. "It can be a difficult time of year," he ventured, diplomatically.

"I'm feeling a bit sorry for myself, that's all," Annie admitted carefully. "Not a good way to be – makes me feel guilty as well…"

Paula had begun pouring tea. "Why so?" She wasn't going to give up and Annie knew hers was a genuine concern. Paula had four kids and a big family. Christmas and New Year were full on for her.

"Well – my sister and her family aren't able to come for New Year this time – the children have gone down with chicken pox and her husband has a bout of man flu – they've decided to batten the hatches and stay home – her words, not mine."

Paula sipped her tea, thoughtfully. "You know you're always welcome to join my mad house," she pointed out, knowing it was at a distance and that meant a taxi or drinking restrictions, always tough at New Year.

"Look – no worries. I'll be alright. The cat and I will snuggle down together, watch TV, raise a glass at midnight and phone the family with greetings. I need to get over myself, that's all."

Paula finished her tea and said little more. "The invitation stands – just saying."

Annie smiled and paid the bill. They put on coats against the December night and hugged in the candlelight.

"So – see you next year – unless you ➔

change your mind…" Paula pecked Rick on the cheek and left to retrieve her car and drive out of the village and home. Rick held the door for Annie and they walked through the cold night together.

"You know…" he ventured somewhere near the river bridge…"You've ever experienced New Year on the other side!"

Annie laughed. She was warm trying to keep pace with him as he strode through the village towards the road where they lived on opposite sides to one another.

"The other side?" she repeated and looked up into the warmth of his face.

"You know that the cottages on my side have rear terraces above the river?"

Getting carried away here. Feeling sorry for yourself and reading something into a long-term friendship? Careful…

"Not as such," he was saying, picking up on her party notion. "Something far more special."

"I'm not sure I follow."

"At midnight, my neighbours all gather on our terraces and patios above the river, raise a glass to each other, watch the fireworks together. It's a really lovely time – and I just thought… as you'll be by yourself…"

Here, he stopped talking and walking. Looked at her steadily and frowned at what to say next.

They'd worked alongside each other but now she saw him in a different light

Annie thought about this. She'd lived in the village for years, but had only moved into her current home a few years back. She loved her cottage and the road, with its chocolate box charm. What difference did a terrace above the river make?

Tactfully, she repeated herself. "The other side," hoping it sounded reflective.

"All I'm saying is – I'd like it if you'd join me on New Year's Eve."

"Are you having a party?"

It was all Anne could think to ask.

She'd known Rick for several years through the community group of volunteers who organised events for the Seniors. They'd worked alongside each other easily and amicably. He'd always been kind and supportive. Reliable. Helpful.

Now, all of a sudden, she found herself looking at him in a new light. Strong and attractive in a rugged sort of way.

Steady on, girl, she admonished herself.

Annie smiled up at him. "Go on."

"You're not making this easy, Annie! How long have we known each other?"

She shrugged.

"How long have I waited for the opportunity to invite you out – and now it's only over to the other side and out onto the terrace – with a meal thrown in beforehand, if you like?"

Ignoring all her previous self-advice, Annie didn't hesitate. "I would like," she told him with a huge smile. "Very much."

I'm cooking my favourite meal – maybe yours, too? We'll see – all you need to do is sit at the table, light candles and enjoy a gastronomic experience…"

Rick grinned, and Annie let herself catch his infectious spirits.

"Then, perhaps we could watch a film?"

Annie shrugged off her thick coat, glad that she'd decided on comfortable jeans.

"I've got a bottle of champagne for midnight as well," he added.

She smiled and looked round. "This is lovely… Do I get to see the terrace yet?"

"Later – ahead of midnight," he said and kissed her cheek, sending a delicious feeling through her whole body. Better than chicken pox and man flu!

"Something smells good," she whispered, eyes shining and not making clear whether she meant the food or his aftershave.

He rewarded her with a knowing grin. "Spaghetti Bolognese – home made," he told her. "This or beans on toast, my second 'go to' dish."

Annie relaxed. "Bolognese wins by a nose," she said, smiling, and sat at the table to light the candles and sip the red wine he poured for her.

"Cheers!"

"To our very special evening," he raised his glass to touch hers and held her gaze for a significant time… "I know I said that the midnight thing is pretty special over on this side – but this is the first time I've made it extra special by sharing it like this."

Annie smiled. There were no words to follow what he'd said.

She'd spent the last few days wondering how the evening would work out, wondering if she'd imagined something in his look and invitation – something that perhaps wasn't there at all.

What she couldn't have imagined was just how well this New Year's Eve was to turn out…

With music and candlelight, home-made food and mellow wine, relaxing with a light-hearted film, close to each other on the sofa – it had been so very different to what she'd thought she'd be doing on this particular evening.

Shortly before midnight, Rick turned on the TV, ready for the chimes of Big Ben. He pulled back the curtains, opened the French windows, carried the champagne and glasses onto the patio.

Annie pulled on her coat and felt only a slight chill on the night air. "Don't forget your jacket… Oh, Rick!…Look!"

Along the row of terraced cottages, his neighbours had done likewise and were now grouped along the railings above the racing river below. There were waves and happy greetings, good wishes and general friendliness.

As the first chimes of midnight rang out from several TVs and phones, theirs was not the only champagne cork popping.

"Happy New Year!"

The words bounced back and forth along the row as the first fireworks flowered against the night sky.

Annie sipped and the sparkling bubbles made her smile. She reached for Rick, held his arm lightly.

His eyes were shining when he looked down at her, moved his arm round her shoulders and kissed her.

"Happy New Year," he murmured. "You OK with this?"

"This moment or…?"

"This moment – and the months ahead," he said. "Looks like it'll be a very different year for us."

"New Year, new ways," she said dreamily. "That's OK by me."

GREAT READS

Why not try our Pocket Novel series, out every fortnight? You'll get a full-length romantic story for just £3.99.

A Series Of Heavens

How many heavens do we all have in our lives – and how could we possibly ever choose just one…?

By Cilla Moss

In my first heaven, there was you, and chocolate, and the highest point of Sheep's Tor on a cold bright day before we knew each other very well but when I was already besotted with you and you kept looking at me with a kind of incredulous joy, as if you couldn't believe we'd found each other either.

However, there wasn't any certainty about each other yet, and there wasn't Frannie, our red setter – a walk isn't a walk without Frannie – and, most of all, there wasn't Mollie and Scott and Jake.

In my second heaven, Mollie is six, and Scott is three, and Jake is one, and we're all playing with a bubble machine in the back garden – the garden I spent the whole year planting and landscaping so

decent night's sleep for about six years.

So my next heaven has a king-sized bed. It's you and me in a hotel room in Rome, with champagne and air conditioning and the kids with their grandparents.

There's one heaven where it's just you and me on the sofa, falling asleep while the news is on, even though it's still light outside, and you pull the blanket down to make sure my feet are warm.

There's a heaven where I'm on my own, drinking coffee from a flask, parked at the beach watching a winter sunset with nowhere else to be.

There's one heaven where I'm very young, and I'm lying between my parents in their bed, and they're playing a game where they take it in turns to say the next

My next heaven has a king-sized bed with champagne and air-conditioning

we'd have privacy and green space and different flowers blooming all year round. But there's no you, because the business is struggling and you're too busy, and this is when we're about to have to move to a small flat near your parents, and every time I look around the garden I'm aware I'm about to lose it.

In addition, you and I haven't had a

line of the story they're telling me. They promised it was a very famous story, but I can tell they're making it up; each line is more and more outlandish. Robots that get the sulks and bears that live in marshmallow caves. I gave up trying to follow the plot ages ago. Now it's just a competition between them to see who can make the other laugh more. The sharp ➔

quick words are flying and there's a back and forth rhythm like dancing. And I'm watching them with joy, hoping with all my heart that I'll have a partner like this one day.

You're not much good with words, my dear, but in one heaven you're making a treehouse for the kids and I could watch you working for hours.

There are heavens with

week so you can't get out of the chair without help, and my knees protest as I try to get up off the floor. Sam takes my hand to help me up, bless him, and I try not to put any weight on his tiny shoulder, adoring the kind heart of him.

So much time has passed.

Jake's moved away, I lost touch with Mary after years of a Christmas card only relationship, and

In one heaven you make a treehouse for the kids and I watch you for hours

Mary, my BFF, where she's plucking my eyebrows and swears she knows what she's doing. And one where there's wild dancing to my favourite song in her bedroom with the boyband posters, and shopping bags all over her duvet, and her little sister trying to copy us, and laughter like I've never laughed again in my life.

However, there's a Maths exam on the horizon with my entire future riding on it, and if it doesn't go well I don't know what I'll do. And – so far – no you to daydream over. I'm pretty sure no one is ever going to want a girl with thighs like mine.

It's tortuous, being seventeen. But oh, the things to look forward to! The bright open space of possibility and all things yet to come.

And of course there's a heaven where our babies have babies. You and me being grandparents: you reading *Guess How Much I Love You* to Lily while Sam and I do a jigsaw. You put your back out last

Frannie is long gone now.

But oh, the lovely memories. There aren't many surprises ahead now. We're settled and secure and very grateful. We have the great comfort of knowing it all turned out well in the end.

So which would I choose if I had to choose one?

It's hard to say. I wish myself forward, I wish myself back. There are no safe places to land. You don't want to get stuck somewhere, no matter how good. But if I can find a place with good memories and something to look forward to, it's somewhere I could be happy. **MW**

. . . .

MY INSPIRATION

I'm lucky enough to live near the sea, and not only does it find the way into my stories quite often, it's a really good place for thinking and getting new ideas.

- ✦ The ancient Greeks invented democracy – "demokratia", or "rule by the people" – however, it only lasted for 185 years.

- ✦ In ancient Greece, prostitutes were recognised for their bright red lipstick – they'd be punished if they did not wear it, to distinguish them from the rest of the non-lipstick wearing women.

- ✦ It was an ancient Greek called Aristarchus of Samos who in the 3rd century first proposed that the planets orbited the sun, and that the stars are distant suns.

- ✦ The ancient Greeks called their land Hellas or Hellada – it was the Romans who referred to it as Greece.

- ✦ Handshakes originated in ancient Greece, its earliest depiction on a 5th century archaeological relief showing Hera and Athena shaking hands.

FANCY THAT!

Fascinating facts on The Great Greeks!

- ✦ Athenian democracy also came up with ostracism, or "ostrakismos", in which the citizens could exile a politician for 10 years if they were deemed a threat to democracy!

- ✦ The ancient Greeks condoned slavery – in fact 40-80% of Athens' population were slaves!

- ✦ In ancient Greece the "unibrow" was considered a sign of beauty and intelligence and women would draw them in with make-up!

- ✦ The humble yo-yo is one of the oldest toys in history, and a vase from the Attica region showing a boy playing with one suggest they may have been invented in ancient Greece.

- ✦ The term "idiot" originated in ancient Greece and was a person who did not participate in political or public arenas.

- ✦ Only the elite ancient Greeks lay on couches to eat – lying down while others served you was considered a sign of power and luxury.

- ✦ The original Olympic Games were in honour of Zeus, and due to its religious significance, it was decreed that no wars would be permitted for the 3 months preceding the games.

- ✦ The first mention of a red carpet was in the 5th century play Agamemnon, which mentions a "crimson path" which could only be walked upon by the gods.

- ✦ Ancient Greek statues were not always white – when they were new the Greeks painted them in bright and vibrant colours.

- ✦ Ancient Greek mathematics, and the discoveries of Pythagoras, Euclid, and Archimedes, are still taught in schools today.

They also traded slaves for salt – hence the common expression, "he's not worth his salt"

Decades Of Love

Romance had entangled Vanessa with this family, no matter how many twists and turns their fates took

By **Della Galton**

Summer 1992

Vanessa held her breath as she stood beside James on the doorstep of the imposing house which had pillars on either side of its gabled porch, a gravel frontage, and lot of windows with the sun glinting off the glass above their heads. The sweet scent of jasmine growing somewhere close by drifted across the summer air.

It had been a long hot drive through the New Forest to get here and then they'd driven along an unmade private road which had woodland on one side and posh houses on the other. Vanessa didn't think she'd ever met anyone who'd lived in a house like this. Let alone gone out with someone whose parents did.

With the hand that wasn't holding the bunch of flowers they'd stopped to buy en route, she reached for James's hand and he squeezed her fingers reassuringly. "Don't look so worried. You've met Dad already and I know Mum will love you." His voice was honey warm.

Vanessa swallowed and hoped her makeup had held up. It tended to melt on hot days.

However, before either of them could say anything else the door swung open and Vanessa was faced with a petite, very

pretty woman. Her flaming red hair was cut in a stylish bob and she was wearing dark trousers and a cream top beneath a pale blue jacket, which Vanessa guessed was linen. Vanessa's first impression of her could be summed up in one word: classy.

"Hi, Mum. This is Vanessa."

"Hello, darling. I thought it might be." She winked at her son and turned the beam of her smile towards Vanessa. "It's so lovely to meet you at last, Vanessa. I'm Suzanne. James has told me so much about you."

"You too," Vanessa said, feeling tongue tied and a little underdressed. She was wearing t-shirt and jeans, albeit the poshest ones she had. She held out the flowers that were wrapped in brown paper and pink ribbon. "These are for you."

"How lovely. Thank you. Come in, come in. Don't stand on ceremony. Let's go through to the back."

Vanessa added the word warmth to the word classy, and she felt herself relax a bit as she stepped into a large hallway that smelled of wood polish with vanilla undertones, alongside James who was grinning like a Cheshire cat.

There were lots of doors, maybe seven or eight on the ground floor, a couple of them open, but most closed and a wide galleried staircase that led up to another floor. Wow, what a contrast to the two up,

Vanessa had never before met anyone who lived in a big, posh house like this

two down house she'd been brought up in.

Suzanne led them into a large country style kitchen that was all oak cupboards and big enough to hold a table that could comfortably seat eight. It smelled of roast dinner with an underlay of herbs, and Vanessa saw pots of basil, coriander and mint lined up on the terracotta windowsill. There was music playing somewhere, something classical, but before Vanessa had time to take in too much, a large yellow Labrador came to greet her, tail wagging frantically.

"Are you OK with dogs, Vanessa? If you're not I can easily put him outside."

"I love dogs." She dropped to her knees to pet his head and his body wriggled in welcome. "What's his name?"

"Toby," James supplied. "He's a right old softie. There's another one somewhere." He whistled through his fingers and a black Labrador bounded in, tail also wagging. "This is Sooty. Not a very original name, I know."

Suzanne was now stirring something on the hob of a cream-coloured Aga. "Maybe you could get Vanessa a drink, James, could you? There's soft or you ➤

could open a bottle of wine? Give your dad a shout – he's out on the terrace, I think. You could take Vanessa out there to say hi."

"Are you sure there's nothing I can help you with?" Vanessa asked her.

"No, love. You go and relax. James, take these dogs with you, will you?"

That was Vanessa's introduction to the McCallum family. All sunshine, friendliness and dogs and a welcome that was warmer than the sun.

It was love she realised when she looked back on it. Proper family love, the like of which she'd never known. She'd been brought up without a dad – he hadn't hung around when her mother had got pregnant so although his name had been on her birth certificate, she'd never met him. Apparently he'd emigrated to New Zealand, leaving his small family in Bournemouth. Then, tragically, Vanessa's mum had died just after Vanessa's eighteenth birthday.

It had meant she'd had to grow up fast. She'd cut short her university plans and got a job in a local property development company in order to support herself. The job was where she'd met James. She'd

On that first visit to his family home James had showed Vanessa the badminton court at the foot of their enormous garden.

"We can have a game after lunch if you fancy it?" he'd said. "I can find you some kit. I'm sure Mum's got something you can borrow."

"Great idea," said Angus, his father, who reminded Vanessa of a great big cuddly bear – at least he did when he wasn't hunched over his desk at work, looking stern.

When their lunch had gone down

The McCallums had proper family love, the like of which she had never known

been immediately drawn to the tall, handsome boy who always had a smile for everyone. In that respect he took after his mum. She hadn't found out until later that James was the big boss's son.

For their first date James had taken her for a meal at a seaside café close to where he shared a flat, and they'd discovered they were both sporty, liked hiking along the Jurassic coastline, and playing badminton.

they'd played badminton and then they'd come back to sit and chat and sunbathe with his parents on the terrace while the dogs dozed and dreamed and the sun shone from a cloudless sky.

Vanessa had felt a real connection with Suzanne. They both adored dogs, in fact animals of all kinds, and they discovered they had a shared ambition.

"I've always wanted a field," Suzanne confessed, "Where I could keep a couple of donkeys and maybe some chickens. It would have a big old chestnut tree in it where I would picnic with my friends."

Vanessa had gestured to the gardens that spread out around them and said, "This lawn is as big as a field. Couldn't you keep chickens and a couple of donkeys here?"

"What about my lawn?" Angus said, raising his eyebrows and giving a mock frown. "I think a badminton court's more use than a field, don't you, Vanessa?"

"Lawns and badminton courts are wonderful," Vanessa agreed and then she and Suzanne had exchanged a secret smile that said, yes but a field with donkeys, chickens and a big old chestnut tree would be better.

You're part of my family now," James had told her after that first meeting. "They'll love you as much as I do. I know they will."

He'd been right, and for the next two and a half years Vanessa had adored being part of the McCallum family.

On her 21st birthday James had asked her to marry him and they'd had a big celebration engagement party at the house, but even as Vanessa had clinked glasses with Suzanne and Angus, she had felt a whisper of foreboding. She and James had been living together for just six months but the cracks in their relationship were already beginning to show.

James was lovely but he'd seemed distant lately. The passion that had characterised their first dates had cooled and she felt as though they'd become more like brother and sister than a newly engaged couple.

There were other differences too. Vanessa longed for green fields and trees and maybe one day children to explore the countryside with, but James wanted the buzz of city life. A family was

something he said he would consider but not until far in the future.

Six months before the wedding Vanessa made the toughest decision she had ever made. She told James she couldn't go through with it. This was made harder because she knew she would have to say goodbye to Suzanne, too.

In time, James would marry some other girl. Suzanne would have some other daughter-in-law with whom to share gossip and dreams on her sunny terrace.

Autumn 2002

Suzanne had been so sad when James and Vanessa had broken off their engagement and had gone their separate ways. She knew her son had really liked the shy, tall girl who loved dogs and the countryside, and who was so different to him. But she had also been sad for herself.

It would have been wonderful to watch James settle down and marry Vanessa and in the fullness of time give her grandchildren to love. But sometimes things weren't to be. To her relief the parting was amicable and so for a while, with James's blessing, she and Vanessa had stayed in touch. But then slowly, as the years had passed, they had drifted apart, their lives moving along different tracks before finally separating completely. Suzanne made friends with the new ladies in James's life, and although none of them quite filled the Vanessa shaped space in her heart, they were nice enough young women.

One by one her friends' sons and daughters married and began their families and Suzanne looked on and tried hard not to feel envious. Although James was rarely without a girlfriend by his side, and he was working hard in the family business, he didn't show any signs of settling down as the millennium ➜

approached and then hurried on past, leaving them all in a new century.

Then, one Saturday afternoon when autumn was plucking handfuls of red and gold leaves from the trees and scattering them across the terrace and Angus was at work – he'd worked a few weekends lately – Suzanne found something that turned her world upside down.

She found a receipt in her husband's jacket which he had left out for dry cleaning. The receipt was for a short break for two in a luxury hotel in Wales. The dates coincided exactly with a fishing trip that Angus had gone to with some old school friends a few weeks earlier.

For a moment Suzanne stood there with the receipt in her hand, frozen in shock. She could feel her heart pumping madly as her thoughts tumbled and swirled and she searched for a rational explanation. There must be one. Surely this couldn't be the cliché it looked like. Surely her steady reliable husband who she'd sworn to love and honour thirty-four years ago couldn't be having an affair.

Her mind flicked back through half a dozen events that hadn't seemed important at the time but which now took on new significance. The late nights at the office, which she had never questioned because Angus had said the business needed him and the money would come in handy. Even though there had never been any evidence of any extra money in their joint bank account.

Then there was the rekindling of a friendship with an old schoolfriend, Kenneth, whom Suzanne had never met, but whom Angus had begun to spend more time with. Kenneth had moved back to Edinburgh where the boys had grown up so Suzanne hadn't been too worried about not meeting him and she'd accepted Angus's trips back to spend time with him.

However, the thing that bothered her the most wasn't a specific event. It was much more intangible. Angus had been distant lately, a little preoccupied. Their lives moved along parallel lines. Suzanne couldn't remember the last time they'd been out for an intimate dinner for two or even the last time he had said he loved her. A few weeks ago he had moved out of the marital bedroom after a summer cold, saying he didn't want to keep her awake with his snoring.

He had never moved back.

Suzanne phoned her husband's mobile but there was no answer. So she picked up a dog lead from the back door and Toby, who was old now and a little arthritic but still up for a walk, came trotting enthusiastically to greet her, his golden feathered tail wagging. They had lost Sooty last year and Suzanne hadn't wanted to bring a young puppy into the house in case it was too much for her faithful old Labrador.

Five minutes later, Suzanne and Toby had crossed the unmade lane and were on their favourite walk on a track through the forest opposite their house.

There was a smell of rich earthy dampness and leaf mulch in the air and Suzanne had to skirt the occasional puddle from the recent rain.

The trees were ablaze in their full autumn glory, although every so often a scattering of leaves would rain down across the path to join their fellows like so many handfuls of red and gold confetti.

Suzanne blinked back tears. She and Angus had got married in the autumn of 1970. In those days her untamed red hair had been a cloud around her shoulders and she'd worn blue-green flowers in her hair to match her eyes and carried an evergreen bouquet. Their wedding had been autumn themed. The bridesmaids had worn bronze-coloured dresses and the balloons that had bedecked the venue had been scarlet and gold.

Was her marriage really over or could Angus still have an explanation? She had

found Angus sitting at the old farmhouse table, with his head in his hands and an overnight bag by his feet and she knew before either of them said a word that it was over. On the table in front of him, where she had left it, lay the receipt for the short break in Wales.

"I'm so sorry," he said, as she shut the back door behind her. "I never meant for it to happen."

Suzanne couldn't believe how calm she was as she sat down opposite him at the table. "Perhaps you had better start at the beginning," she said.

That conversation still seemed surreal, weeks and months after it had taken place. The conversation where Suzanne had learned that Kenneth from Edinburgh was actually Kara from Cardiff. That the affair had been going on much longer than she'd realised, almost four and a half years. That she wasn't quite the last to know – James hadn't guessed what was happening either, but that a great many other people had known.

Surely her reliable husband of thirty-four years couldn't be having an affair?

followed up the unanswered call with a text saying there was something they needed to discuss and what time did he think he'd be in? But there had been no answer to this either. At least not yet.

So now, she walked through the forest, with her dog, letting the peace of the autumnal day wrap around her and soothe her until her thoughts slowly quietened.

When she got back to the house she saw that Angus had beaten her back. His car was in the drive. She touched the bonnet as she passed, still warm, so he hadn't been back long.

She let herself in the back door and

Angus insisted he loved her still, that he'd always loved her as a friend. And that was the reason he hadn't told her sooner.

After the initial red-hot anger of betrayal and pain had cooled, because whatever Angus said, Suzanne knew it had been fear he'd lose everything, not love, that had stopped him from telling her, she had come around to a gradual acceptance of it all. Angus might be a coward and an adulterer, at least she was young enough to start again. She was only fifty-two.

While the divorce and house sale went through. Suzanne rented a cottage in Ringwood in Dorset and thought about ➜

what she wanted to do with the rest of her life. She and James grew closer. She kept her feelings about his adulterous father to herself. Angus may have behaved badly but he would always be James's father.

She didn't think she wanted to marry again, but there were other things she did want to do. She remembered an old dream she'd had, how she had wanted a field with donkeys, and chickens and a big old spreading chestnut tree.

And for the first time in a long while she thought about Vanessa and wondered how she was getting on.

"It's funny you should mention Vanessa," James said when they were having Sunday lunch together one day, "Because I happened to bump into her a few weeks ago."

He frowned and put his head on one side, adding, "She's just got married and they have a little one. I can put you in touch with her again, if you like?"

Winter 2012

Vanessa looked out of her window as she washed up the breakfast things at a garden that was blanketed with snow, and smiled. Through the square of her kitchen window she could see Max, her six-year-old, stomping through the pristine whiteness. It was December 20th and it had snowed all night – a rare occurrence in Dorset. Max had been so excited, she'd barely managed to get his wellington boots and coat on before he'd dashed outside.

Now, as she looked out of the window, he looked up at her and their gazes met. "Three, two, one," she counted under her breath before the back door burst open and he raced into the kitchen in an energy burst of chill air.

"Mummy can you help me build a snowman? Pleeeeeze."

"Of course I can, darling."

"Can we do it now?"

"Is it alright if I just take a second to put my gloves on first?"

Max jiggled from foot to foot. "Hurry up – please."

Then they were both hurrying out to the garden, their breath puffing out into the freezing air and their laughter joining with the rest of Vanessa's neighbours as all the kids in the neighbourhood, both young and young at heart, joined in with the fun.

For the next twenty minutes they focused on making a snowman. When he was built, Vanessa helped Max to find pebbles for his eyes and his smile and she went into the house to get a carrot for his nose and an old scarf that was hanging on the hook in the hall.

Later that day, Max's father was coming to pick him up – it was his weekend. He'd promised to take Max tobogganing if the forecast snow arrived. Vanessa's marriage to Max's father had been brief. Simon had been on the rebound when they'd met, not really ready for a new relationship. Max hadn't been planned and though they'd tried to make it work as a couple, it never did.

Fortunately, though, and unlike Vanessa's own father, Simon had wanted to be part of his son's life. Vanessa adored being a mum and co-parenting was working much better than she'd hoped. It wasn't ideal but it was alright, and she was happy.

Another good thing that had happened since she'd had Max was that she'd got back in touch with Suzanne again.

They'd started meeting up not long after Max had been born and it had been brilliant to rekindle her friendship with the older woman.

L ife doesn't always work out as you plan," Suzanne had said when they'd first met up again. "But the way I look at it is nothing is ever wasted. As my old mother-in-law used to say, 'What's for you won't go past you'. It's an old Scottish saying," she said smiling her lovely smile. "It means that if something is meant to be, then it will happen, no matter what,

in a bowl, gathered from her allotment. She pauses for a moment to stretch her arms above her head and enjoy the spring sunshine on her face.

To her right, Suzanne is also sitting in a deckchair with her iPad on her lap. She is busy scrolling through brochures of mother of the groom outfits for the forthcoming wedding.

"What do you think of this one?" she asks Vanessa, passing her the device.

"It's gorgeous. Perfect for your hair. It's a yes from me," Vanessa says.

"It's a yes from me too," James says, coming closer and leaning over his mother's shoulder. He's greying at the temples these days and it suits him.

So does the man who is never far from his side: Alan, a quiet, sensitive man with a wicked sense of humour, who is perfect for James. Vanessa has thought this since the moment James introduced them. Alan and James are getting married in three month's time. Vanessa is glad James has

They'd gone for a coffee for old time's sake and caught up on the missing years

it's just that it may not happen in quite the way you expect."

It was good being back in James's life too, Vanessa had thought. It had surprised her to learn that he had never married. They'd gone for a coffee in a farm shop in Ringwood, just for old times sake, and over the heady scent of donuts and gingerbread lattes – which it turned out they both loved – they had caught up on the missing years.

Spring 2022

V anessa is sitting on a deckchair beneath the spreading boughs of a chestnut tree. She is cleaning radishes

finally discovered who he really is.

Vanessa and Max – who is now sixteen – will be on the top table with Suzanne, because as Suzanne frequently points out, Vanessa feels like the daughter she never had, and Max feels like the grandchild she never had, although she hasn't completely abandoned the idea of James providing her with grandchildren now he's finally settling down.

Simon will be there too. Vanessa and Simon got back together just after their son turned seven, and they have been together ever since.

"It's funny how things work out," Suzanne told Vanessa now. "When you and James split up I never dreamed ➤

you would end up back in my life again, but now here we are, with our houses just a stone's throw from each other. I'm so glad you're in my life, Vanessa."

"Likewise," Vanessa said, feeling her throat close a little at the love in the older woman's eyes. She and Simon had recently bought a house that abutted Suzanne's. There are just the allotments between them – and a field which houses three grey donkeys.

"I'm so glad you got your donkeys too," Vanessa adds, "Even if they're not technically yours."

"Chickens are probably easier to look after," Suzanne agrees, as a brown feathered hen wanders close by, pecking at the grass near their feet.

As if on cue the braying sound of a

Suzanne and she have shared most things.

"What's for you won't go by you," Vanessa says to James, putting down the bowl of radishes and standing up from her deckchair to stretch. "Isn't that what your mum always says."

James nods, glancing across at his mother, who is laughing with Dan now,

"It's funny how things work out," she said. "What's for you won't go by you"

donkey cuts through the air and Suzanne gets to her feet, smiling. "Dan must be here," she said.

"Dan brays like a donkey?" Alan quips and Suzanne shoots him a mock stern glance. "They know a treat's coming," she says as a white-haired man appears at the gate on the other side of the field and the donkeys trot eagerly to greet him.

Alan and James exchange smiles as Suzanne goes to meet Dan, and when she's out of earshot, James says, "I think my mother's rather keen on Dan."

He catches Vanessa's eye, adding, "What do you think? Is it my imagination or does she light up when he's about?"

"It's not your imagination," Vanessa says. "Definitely not."

She has noticed it too, the sparkle in his mother's eyes – and in fact she also has some inside information, because over the years, especially the last two decades

her elbows resting on the wooden fence. Their voices are too low for anyone to pick out the words.

Three decades she has been involved with this family, Vanessa thinks. There has been heartbreak for all of them but sitting here now in Suzanne's sunny garden under the spreading boughs of the chestnut tree she thinks only of the love. Three decades of love, binding them together, and as the soft spring air touches her face she feels only hope for the decades that are yet to come. (MW)

. . . .

MY INSPIRATION

I'm inspired by my surroundings, especially the Dorset countryside, so walking with my dogs is brilliant. I spend many an hour tramping through fields in all seasons working out knotty plot problems.

Fruit Curd

52 Calories per tbsp

Ingredients (Makes about 575g)
For Lemon and Lime Curd:
- ◆ **3 limes**
- ◆ **2 lemons**
- ◆ **2 large eggs and**
- ◆ **2 large egg yolks**
- ◆ **250g caster sugar**
- ◆ **100g butter**

1 Grate the rind from 1 lime and 2 lemons. Squeeze the juice from the limes and lemons and place in a heatproof bowl with the rinds. Add the eggs, sugar and butter.

2 Place over a pan of simmering water and stir with a wooden spoon until the sugar dissolves. Continue stirring until thick enough to coat the back of the spoon.

3 Pour through a sieve into a clean jug and then into sterilised jars. Cover and store in the fridge. Use within 2-3 weeks.

For Orange Curd:
Use 2tbsp lemon juice, the juice of 3 oranges and the grated rind or 1 orange instead of the limes and lemons. Follow the method above. ➞ 79

The Dating Dilemma

Having only just started seeing Gemma, Simon was all in a quandary over what to do for Valentine's Day!

By Kath Kilburn

Simon lay in bed, relishing the early morning quiet. Any minute seven year old Arlo would wake, ready for fun. That was fine, but for now Simon wanted to play over in his mind last night's dinner, his first evening with Gemma. Had it really gone as well as he thought? She'd giggled when he'd knocked over that glass of red; if anything it had broken the ice. She was fresh as a summer morning, with dark, hair, clear, green eyes and a dimpled smile.

Valentine's Day was coming up. Could he ignore it, pretend he'd thought they were too new an item? After all, they'd only been out once!

"Is Gemma your girlfriend, Dad?"

Arlo launched himself onto Simon's bed and started firing off a series of questions.

"Arlo, we only went out for the first time last night!"

"But would you like her to be your girlfriend?" He wanted to get this straight.

"Well, I'm going to ring her tomorrow and I hope we're going to go out again, so maybe if she says yes, then we can call her my girlfriend, OK?"

Arlo already knew Gemma, who worked at his after school club, so there'd been no chance of keeping the fledgling relationship quiet. Simon was keen not to spook her with his son's enthusiasm – Arlo made no secret of his longing for a new mum!

"I hope she does say yes, Dad," he said thoughtfully. "She's really nice."

Later, Simon was in the local card shop and headed for the Valentine's Day selection. With his plan for dinner at a local bistro accepted, he thought he'd best check them out. So many cards, so little idea what might be right for Gemma. He left the shop in despair. Maybe it'd be easier to choose nearer the time.

Sipping double espressos after the bistro meal two days later, Gemma reached across and took his hand. "I've really enjoyed tonight. Can we do this again? My treat next time."

His heart jumped a little. "That'd be great," Simon answered and they set a date for a football match, followed by pie and peas, a tradition in Gemma's family.

"Why not bring Arlo?" she asked. "I know he likes football."

Before the match, Simon still had Valentine's Day to sort. He wandered back to the card shop. As he studied the selection, his mind racing through the options, he heard voices from the other side of the rack. Specifically, Gemma's voice and that of her colleague at Arlo's primary school. They were heading towards his aisle. Quickly he turned on his heel to face the birthday cards.

"Hi, Simon! What are you doing here?"

Will you be my Valentine?

She was smiling. Or maybe laughing, because he could feel the pinkness in his face and the "hi" he was attempting was stuck in his throat.

"This is my friend, Lucy." Gemma turned. "Lucy, Simon."

Lucy smiled. "Hi Simon, I've heard some good stuff about you."

Simon managed a less than sparkly response and slunk off with the excuse of seeking a birthday card for his brother. He was dejected by his performance, but one bit of information stuck in his head. Gemma had told her friend about him…

He decided he'd think about a card, maybe flowers too, after the match date. He'd see how they got on in a casual daytime setting, with Arlo in tow too – that would alter the dynamic a bit. Crikey, why was he so wound up about this Valentine's Day thing? Maybe it was that in-between stage, that feeling of being pretty sure she liked him, but not sure how much? He gave himself a stern talking to: *We're having a good time. Let's just enjoy it while it lasts, and stop stressing over a stupid card.*

He felt better – until he was putting Arlo to bed that night. His son didn't go in for reflection usually – he was more interested in swings and slides and climbing trees – but the time they spent chatting at the day's end brought out his thoughtful side.

"Mrs Jones at school told us about St Valentine today and how he used to marry soldiers when he wasn't supposed to. That's why he got into trouble."

"That was a very long time ago, Arlo."

Arlo looked up at his dad. "That's ➡

why we buy cards for people if we like them or love them. That's why it's called Valentine's Day. So…are you sending Gemma a card for Valentine's Day?"

"We'll see, son," was the best Simon could manage. So far, he didn't seem able to buy one, never mind actually send it.

"Dad?" Arlo was sounding sleepy now. "It'd be great, wouldn't it, if we had Gemma living here with us? Like a mummy?"

"Let's not get ahead of ourselves, Arlo," said Simon, but he couldn't help smiling as he left the room.

The football match went fine. Arlo had a great time and managed not to make any inappropriate remarks about wanting Gemma around long-term. Holding hands together, with his son running along in front, seemed both new and charmingly natural to Simon and he revelled in the

on *Feb 14th?* was hardly romantic. OK, just a card, then.

While Arlo played with the boy next door, Simon drove to the bigger shop in the next town and finally bought a card. It featured a panda wearing a tiara, and he wasn't sure it was just right, so he also bought one with a cushioned gingham heart on it. Was that a bit serious though? So he bought a joke one– and one that played a few creaky bars of *Unchained Melody*… and a couple of others. Back home, he threw them on the worktop. The Big Day was fast approaching and he was as confused as ever. Why couldn't he be a smooth guy who automatically knew the right thing to do?

Gemma went to aerobics on Thursday evenings and, with her car in the garage, Simon had offered to pick her up, and suggested a quick drink on the way home. His kindly next door neighbour

Why couldn't he be the smooth type who always knew the right thing to do?

ordinariness of the situation, cheering and groaning at the same points during the match, and enjoying the pie and peas with Gemma's family afterwards.

"I enjoyed that, Dad," Arlo said as they walked home. "Thanks for taking me."

Simon's heart melted. He knew how much that enjoyment had been increased by Gemma being there. And he could empathise with that, because he wanted her to stay around as well. Very much.

Forget the card. He'd book a weekend away for the two of them. Or was that too soon? No, maybe just chocolates. That might look mean though. Jewellery maybe? This was so important – relationships had broken down over less. He could ask her but, *What sort of surprise would you like*

was babysitting with strict instructions to keep up the pretence to Arlo that his dad was out with the lads. His questions were getting a bit much lately, and Simon would prefer not to have to go through the same stuff again in the morning.

"Thanks for this, Simon – I don't like missing class," Gemma said, between sips of red wine.

"No worries." He smiled at her, thinking how good it felt to be here with this gorgeous woman… who was suddenly looking rather sheepish.

"Simon…" she started and then paused, seemingly unsure.

He hoped this wasn't bad news.

"How can I say this? Look, I'll just come out with it. Valentine's Day's coming up, right? I just wanted to say, please don't arrange anything. All the men in my past who've done lavish stuff for St Valentine's… well, it's all turned out to be just for show and it didn't mean anything, and then we've split up soon after."

She stroked the inside of his wrist, seeming to search for the right words, then continued, "Can we just ignore it? I'm not really into all that fake romantic stuff. So let's just treat it like any other day. No presents, no cards, no surprises. Is that OK with you? Or am I just a big killjoy?"

She looked up at him, the uncertainly in those green eyes making Simon pause, but only until he got his feelings under control.

"Yes," he finally said. "I'm fine with that We can do the romantic stuff just when it suits us. And it won't be fake, I promise."

Gemma took up her theme again, "Romance is more about everyday things – like you coming to pick me up tonight. That means more to me than a card. I love dressing up, weekends away, dinner dates, all that kind of thing, but this is the long-term stuff, isn't it? This is what shows someone's character, whether they care."

This time he really was speechless. She'd actually said "long-term".

Did you have a nice time with Gemma, Dad?" Arlo asked next morning. It turned out he'd heard already that they were meeting, from Gemma herself.

"Yes, thanks, son."

"Will you be sending her a Valentine's card then, like Mrs Jones said?"

"Mrs Jones said I had to send Gemma a card?" Simon asked incredulously.

"No, silly! She said it about everyone who likes somebody a lot."

"Me and Gemma – we've decided we're

not bothering with cards and presents, Arlo, If that's OK with you?"

Arlo looked like it wasn't, but said nothing more. There was the business of finding the plastic soldier in the Rice Krispies to attend to.

On St Valentine's Day itself, Simon relaxed and thought how lucky it was that Gemma had brought the subject out in the open. How he loved her honesty, and how wonderful her nervousness had made him feel. How perfect she was altogether! He was brought down to earth by a ring at the doorbell, and there she stood, card in hand.

"I told you I didn't need a card." She grinned and waved the card in front of him playfully.

"I didn't send one," he said, confused.

Gemma laughed. "No, I know… But look at this though…" she said, opening the envelope.

Simon spotted a crayoned red rose and could make out Arlo's careful, unsteady handwriting.

"Dear Gemma," she read out to him, "I like love you a lot, Simon xxx."

It took Simon a while to recover, but when he did, for once he found exactly the right words…

"I couldn't have put it better myself, Gemma!" Ⓜ

MY INSPIRATION

Inspiration comes from anywhere and everywhere, from the general – changing seasons etc – through to those overheard quirky quotes, to tiny-but-significant details: matching toothbrushes perhaps.

Easter Parade

It looks as though busy bunny Bree has ended up with a lot more than eggs in her basket…

By Julie Dawn Baker

"You've got to be kidding!" Mum protests as I dump my carrier bags on the dining table and ask for her help. "Don't tell me…" She eyes me suspiciously. "Amanda is behind all this, isn't she?"

Amanda is my best friend, but Mum's not exactly a fan. So, I'm reluctant to explain why on the Thursday before Easter, I've come home with metres of purple and green coloured fabric and bundles of tape that need to be sewn into bunting for the Fentons' Family Easter Eggstravaganza in two days' time.

"Of course, I'll help you, Bree," Mum

eye on the goal from when we were teenagers – and look at her now. An up-and-coming lawyer with Fentons – a large, high-profile legal firm.

And, thanks to Amanda, I work for Fentons too. Not as a lawyer. I'm their receptionist AKA general dogsbody.

It's not my ideal job. I spend a lot of time photocopying, filing, smiling – often at people that I'm not sure I like very much. But all things considered, it's a good place to work. For now.

Although, let's be honest, I'm running out of time to make something of my life. I left school with three decent A-levels and planned on becoming a teacher. But instead of going to university, I took a gap

I spend a lot of time smiling – often at people I'm not sure I like very much

sighs, "but it's about time you stopped letting Amanda take advantage of you. She's always been the same, ever since you two were at school."

Despite what Mum thinks, Amanda is a good friend. We have each other's backs. If it wasn't for her, I wouldn't have the best job I've had in a while.

I guess I'm a bit of a late bloomer. Not like Amanda. She's always been much more focused – had her

year, which turned into much more than a year. I did a lot of travelling, and I've had a series of stopgap jobs. A little bit of this. A little bit of that. Time flies when you're having fun, they say.

And now… I'll be thirty next birthday, and I'm still living at home with Mum. I really need to get my act together and think seriously about a proper career.

Definitely nothing to do with sewing, though, I decide, when Mum and I begin cutting out triangles from the fabric spread across the dining table.

"So how come you got lumbered with ➡

making bunting?" Mum asks, as our pile of purple and green triangles gradually grows. "This can't be part of your job description!" She snorts.

"No, this is because I'm on the social committee…"

Amanda press-ganged me into joining the social committee, and usually I'm asked to produce flyers, send out information, book venues. Nothing too challenging.

Then came the Fentons' Family Easter Eggstravaganza. It's a family fun day with an Easter theme, and not just for Fentons' employees, but clients and their families too. A big deal. Potentially a logistical nightmare. Nonetheless, Amanda had eagerly taken the lead.

Unfortunately… how can I put this? She'd dropped a few balls. Nothing major in my view. I mean, did it really matter that we didn't have bunting in Fentons' brand colours? Apparently, it did! According to Amanda, it was a disaster of monumental proportions.

"Your mum's got a sewing machine, though, hasn't she?" Amanda looked at me expectantly.

"Yes…" I admitted hesitantly.

"Perfect! I knew I could count on you." Amanda perked right up. "And you'll have time to sort out the guest passes, won't you?" she added, depositing a box of empty lanyards on my desk. "And can you pick up the Easter Bunny outfit from the fancy-dress place?"

"Weren't you supposed to collect the bunny costume?"

"No time. Client meetings all afternoon." Amanda pulled a sad face. "And it's best if you collect the costume, because you'll be wearing it on the day."

"Me! I thought you were…"

"Change of plan. You'll be a much better Easter Bunny. You're organising the games and the egg hunt, after all. I'm hosting the event, so I'll have to make announcements, welcome everyone, and it might be hard to hear what I'm saying if I'm in costume," she pointed out.

"I told the woman who phoned, you're lucky to get any sort of rabbit costume"

"What are we going to do?" She'd cornered me in reception at lunchtime almost in tears and furious that the custom bunting supplier had let us down. She'd also been quick to point out that it had been me who had found the company on the internet.

Feeling a tiny bit guilty that perhaps I hadn't done my due diligence in researching the supplier, I rashly suggested that we might be able to get some fabric in Fentons' colours and make the bunting ourselves. Amanda loved this idea … only she had a prior arrangement that she couldn't break – plus, she didn't have a sewing machine.

"Besides, the characters at Disneyland never talk, do they?"

Fentons' Easter event was hardly Disneyland, but I didn't argue.

Later, when I picked up the costume, it turned out that Amanda hadn't reserved an Easter Bunny suit after all.

"I don't think this is right," I protested when they gave me a White Rabbit from *Alice In Wonderland* costume – the red waistcoat and pocket watch were dead giveaways. "I'm sorry, but we ordered an Easter Bunny."

The shop assistant rolled her eyes.

"I explained to the woman who phoned earlier that we were all out of

Easter Bunnies. It's that time of year," she added sarcastically. "I told her, you're lucky to get any sort of rabbit, leaving it this late to order."

"But we ordered ages ago…"

"No, just this morning."

"This morning!" We'd been planning the Easter Eggstravaganza for months.

"If you carry a wicker basket filled with eggs, no one will notice," the assistant suggested.

I stopped at the pound shop and bought a bright pink wicker basket and a big bag of mini eggs, and … let's just say, I'm not convinced. But it's too late to do anything about it now.

I haven't mentioned the lanyards or the costume fiasco to Mum. I know she'll have something cutting to say.

Come Saturday morning, I'm quite excited. This event is right up my street, organising games and the egg hunt.

When I was travelling, I did quite a few jobs working with kids – camp counsellor in America, day care at a ski resort in Canada, and even a stint at Bognor Butlin's as a Redcoat one year. Children, I find, are generally a lot more fun to work with than adults.

That's not to say they're uncritical

though, and I'm a bit worried about the bunny costume. I decide to try it on at the last minute to get Mum's reaction.

She gives a little shriek when an oversized rabbit wearing a red waistcoat and white gloves appears in the kitchen. "Goodness! I thought you were supposed to be the Easter Bunny, not the White Rabbit," she jokes.

I hold up my basket of Easter eggs.

"Not convinced?" I ask, and don't mention that Amanda left it until the last minute to rent the costume.

"Oh dear, oh dear," Mum mutters, and I'm not sure if she's imitating the White Rabbit or genuinely concerned about my outfit. "No one will notice if we tuck the pocket watch out of sight," she says and makes the adjustment. "Right, are you ready to roll?"

"Give me a minute to get changed."

"No time for that," Mum says, glancing anxiously at the clock.

Fentons' Easter event is being held at a country park a few miles out of town. It's on a bus route, but not exactly convenient, especially when I'm transporting bunting, lanyards and other paraphernalia necessary for the day. Luckily, though, Mum's agreed to →

drop me off there on her way to work.

"I'll put the bunting and your work stuff in the boot," Mum tells me, grabbing her car keys. "Have you got everything else you need?"

I grab my clothes for later, pick up my handbag, and head out to the car.

"Make sure that Amanda does her fair share of the work today!" Mum warns when she drops me at the park gates. She pops open the boot so I can retrieve the box of bunting and lanyards. "It's about time you…"

Her words are lost as a lorry roars by, but I get her drift. Slamming the boot shut,

Amanda says when she turns up an hour later, at the same time as Tim from Conveyancing. They are the last members of the social committee to arrive.

I've had a couple of casual dates with Tim. I quite like him. Although I'm not sure how he feels about me being the firm's receptionist. I was hoping that I'd get to spend a bit more time with him this evening. After the main event, the social committee are all going out for drinks and tapas. A sort of wrap party.

Obviously, I can't go dressed as a rabbit. Hopefully, Amanda will drive me home to change my clothes later. I don't

I was hoping I'd get to spend a bit more time with Tim over the drinks and tapas

I'm juggling my box and bunny headpiece when I see the indicator blinking, hear the engine revving, and realise that Mum is accelerating into the busy Saturday morning traffic.

"Wait!" I shout, but it's too late.

Never one to over-use her rear-view mirror, Mum hits the road – with my handbag, clothes and shoes still in the back seat. If she notices me jumping up and down waving madly, she obviously thinks I'm just miming an enthusiastic goodbye because, although I wait at the park entrance for a while, she doesn't turn the car round and come back.

I'd call her, but you've guessed it – my phone is in my bag, which is in the car.

"Your costume looks… great!"

ask her now, though, because she has pulled out a clipboard and is checking off items on her list.

The bunting has been strung around our designated area, the food trucks are in place, the face painter is ready to transform little faces, the games area is set up, and hundreds of eggs have been hidden for the egg hunt.

"But where's the balloon artist?" Amanda frowns.

"I think this is him now," I reassure her and wave at the tall man dressed in jeans, white shirt, a rainbow-coloured waistcoat and a nifty top hat who is wheeling a large silver case towards us.

"Show him where to set up, Bree. I'll need you to hand out the guest passes

as people arrive. And remember to stay in character." Amanda issues brisk instructions and hurries off, leaving me to meet and greet.

"Hi! You must be the balloon artist."

"I am! Ben, the balloon bender. Corny, I know, but helps people remember me." He doffs his hat in best showman tradition and flashes me a twinkly grin.

Once the guests begin to arrive, we quickly form a double act, with me handing out passes and Ben delighting children and adults alike with balloon bunnies and a myriad of other inflatable creations.

Fentons' Easter event is soon in full swing, and everyone is having fun. I'm relieved when the egg and spoon races are a hit, and of course, everyone enthusiastically joins in the egg hunt.

When he's not twisting balloons, Ben helps me organise the children's games, and I'm glad of the help because, apart from when she's announcing the various activities, Amanda is noticeably absent. I see her chatting with some of Fentons' partners, and even spot her pretending to position the bunting as Tim takes her picture, but as for doing any actual work… Let's just say, I should probably have listened to Mum.

I'm taking a break in the shade of some trees and don't mean to eavesdrop when I overhear Mr Fenton Senior congratulating Amanda.

"Well done, Amanda! Excellent job organising a very successful event! The bunting in Fentons' brand colours was a very nice touch."

"Thank you." I hear the pride in Amanda's voice.

"Just one thing. The Easter Bunny is wearing a White Rabbit costume. A small detail, but small details are important in our business. Doesn't convey quite the right impression…"

"Absolutely," Amanda agrees. "I'll have a word with Bree. She didn't order the costume in time, and this was all that was available on such short notice. I'm very sorry, but there wasn't a lot I could do."

Honestly, I'm speechless.

The rest of the day loses its sparkle, and I'm glad when everyone starts to drift away. Parents shepherd tired children to waiting cars, and the singles start making plans to depart.

I'm expecting everyone from the social committee to help with the clean-up, but I notice some of them slinking off in the direction of the car park too.

"Time for drinks and tapas!" Tim says, looking at Amanda.

"Would you drop me home first, please? Obviously, I can't go dressed like this." Feeling a bit stupid, I explain how Mum drove off with my bag and change of clothes this morning.

Tim looks embarrassed.

"Er, the problem is, if we give you a lift home, we'll be late …"

"Yes," Amanda backs him up. "The restaurant won't hold our reservation. Really sorry, Bree…" ➤

"The thing is, I don't have my phone, or any money…"

"No problem!" Tim pulls out his wallet and hands me a ten-pound note.

"See you later!" Amanda says with a smile, and I notice Tim drape his arm around her shoulders as they hurry away.

"Hey, what about the bunting?" I call after them, but drinks and tapas await.

"I'll help," a now familiar voice offers.

"Thanks, Ben."

Everyone has left, so at last I take off my headpiece. I know I'm not looking my best. Messed-up hair, flushed, a little sweaty. But I can tell from Ben's smile that none of that matters.

"I like working with kids," I confess, "but I think I've left it a bit late to go back to studying. I'd have to do a degree, the teacher training…"

"It's never too late," he says emphatically, picking up the pocket watch and handing it to me. "There were lots of people much older than you on my teaching course," he adds. "Never mind the Easter Bunny, you were like the Pied Piper with the kids during the egg hunt. They loved you!"

"That might have had something to do with chocolate being involved," I laugh.

He shakes his head. "No, you're a natural. Look, I'm meeting friends later,

"You were like the Pied Piper with the kids during the egg hunt. They loved you"

Together we take down the bunting, roll it up, and stow it in my box of tricks. We pick up pieces of stray litter and dump them into a nearby bin.

"Need a lift home?" he asks.

"If it's not too far out of your way…"

"Not at all," he assures me, even though I haven't told him where I live.

Walking towards the car park, he says, "You're good with kids. If you weren't a lawyer, you'd have made a wonderful teacher."

"I'm not a lawyer!" I laugh, then add more seriously, "D'you really think I'd make a good teacher?"

"I do. And I should know. Balloon twisting is a part-time gig for me – I'm a junior school teacher."

"Really?"

I imagine he's popular with his pupils.

We've reached Ben's car. As we're stowing our things in the boot, the White Rabbit's timepiece falls out of my waistcoat pocket.

and some of them are teachers. Why not come along? I'd love you to meet them… Actually, forget them, I want to get to know you."

I hesitate. Ben looks disappointed.

"Of course, you probably want to join your colleagues…"

I think about Amanda, Tim, and the others having their drinks and tapas, and I think about Amanda's earlier betrayal.

"No, actually I don't," I tell him truthfully. "I'd love to come out with you and meet your friends."

Turning the pocket watch over in my hands, I study it for a moment.

It is time, I realise, to start making new friends – and maybe it's time to start thinking about a new career. 🅜🅦

MY INSPIRATION

Family and friends are my greatest source of inspiration. It is often the funny things they say or do which make me think, *I feel a story coming on!*

Brain Boosters

Missing Link

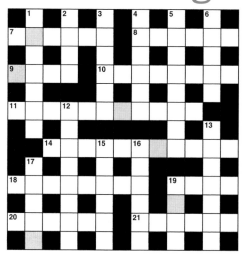

The answer to each clue is a word which has a link with each of the three words listed. This word may come at the end (eg **HEAD** linked with **BEACH, BIG, HAMMER**), at the beginning (eg **BLACK** linked with **BEAUTY, BOARD** and **JACK**) or a mixture of the two (eg **STONE** linked with **HAIL, LIME** and **WALL**).

ACROSS

7 Gun, Mixer, Portland (6)
8 Crop, Farmer, Land (6)
9 Sun, Tone, Up (4)
10 Car, Investigator, Minor (8)
11 Public, Speech, Voice (11)
14 Building, Government, Safety (11)
18 Leather, Mints, Tobacco (8)
19 Gap, Leap, Light (4)
20 Furniture, Scarab, Stag (6)
21 Hard, Income, Well (6)

DOWN

1 Ingenious, Labour-saving, Mechanical (7)
2 Big, Raw, Real (4)
3 Back, Eye, Muscle (6)
4 Lucky, Regimental, Team (6)
5 Chicken, Naan, Oven (8)
6 Glass, Lock, Stone (5)
12 Cheese, Pan, Spanish (8)
13 Otherwise, Signal, Tone (7)
15 Front, Manchester, Nations (6)
16 Fall, Fast, Sound (6)
17 Burnt, Coloured, Raw (5)
19 Minster, New, Stone (4)

Turn To Page 157 For Solutions

Hidden word in the shaded squares: _____

Waiting For The Wedding

How can a casual, barbed comment from a psychic at a wedding be more powerful than Tom's love?

By Sarah Swatridge

When are you going to make an honest woman of the girl?" Grandpa asked Tom.

"I keep asking, but she won't have me."

"Really?" his grandfather answered. "You've been together for years. What's the problem?"

Tom took a deep breath and sat at the kitchen table. He put his head in his hands.

"It's so stupid really," he began. "About five years ago we went to her best friend's wedding. She was a bridesmaid."

"Pink dress?" Gran nodded to herself as though she were picturing the photo.

Liz that. The woman had never met us. She'd probably argued with her own boyfriend and was feeling miserable."

"But Liz believed what she said?" Gran asked him quietly.

Tom nodded and looked down at his ring-less hands.

Two months later Liz was sitting at the corner table in the café waiting for Tom. He was late, which wasn't like him, but it had been pouring all day. Maybe the main road had been flooded again?

The bell over the café door chimed as a tall redhead made her entrance. Her coat dripped puddles as she wriggled out of it

"I won't stay long." Nevertheless the woman slid into the seat opposite her

"That's right," Tom smiled at the memory. "Well, at the reception there was this weird woman. Tall and thin with long red hair and nails to match. She was part of the band, she played saxophone."

His grandparents looked at each other and back at Tom, "We were all sitting down after the speeches and this woman looked straight at Liz and said, 'It's no use marrying him, it won't work.'"

"Silly woman," Grandpa said. "What does she know?"

"Exactly!" echoed Tom. "I keep telling

and headed straight towards the corner table… and Liz.

Liz recognised her at once from Becky's wedding. She was filled with a feeling of doom and gloom. Had something dreadful happened to Tom?

"Don't worry," the woman said. "I shan't stay long." Nevertheless she slid into the chair opposite Liz. "I don't know if you remember me,"

"I do," Liz told her. "And I don't think we have anything to say to each other."

"Well you're wrong there," the woman

wiped raindrops from her forehead. "I'll be honest with you. I can't remember exactly what I said. I meet loads of people and sometimes I pick up vibes or get a feeling and I feel it's my duty to say something."

"And ruin their lives?"

"You didn't have to listen… or take me seriously."

"It was too late. You'd already put a curse on our relationship – telling us it would never work."

The woman leaned forward across the table and met Liz's distrustful eye.

"I'm sorry for what I said. And even more upset that you took it to heart. If the truth be told I have a lot of premonitions, but I never follow them up to see whether I was right… or not. It's not like I'm on Trip Advisor and people can leave a review. I must have picked up on ➡

something negative that day."

"The bride and groom split up last year," Liz said.

"Well, perhaps that was it. Who knows, maybe I'd had too much to drink? But I'm stone cold sober now and I'm telling you to forget it. Understand?"

"Has he told you to say this?" Liz asked suspiciously.

"Better than that, he paid me!" The woman slapped a brown envelope down on the table.

Liz bit her lip. What did Tom think he was playing at?

"I think you've said enough. Please go."

The redhead stood and reached for her sopping wet coat.

"I will tell you something for nothing.

said quietly, his dark eyes fixed on her.

Liz looked at his dripping, tousled hair. She wanted to run her fingers through it and kiss his damp lips.

"Try me," she said.

As if in slow motion, Tom sank to one

"I think that anyone who goes to that much trouble must be crazy about you"

I've moved house four times since that wedding and changed my name. It must have taken quite a bit of detective work for him to track me down. I think that anyone who goes to that much trouble must be crazy about you. Just think about it."

With that the woman slid the envelope across the table towards Liz.

"I can't take his money. He's done me a favour. I've always assumed people want their fortunes told and I never charge, but now I'll ask first before I jump in. Put the money towards the wedding."

With that, the woman disappeared.

Liz looked up from the brown envelope lying on the café table. Tom was standing there with a ring box in his hand. She hadn't even noticed him arrive.

"I won't embarrass you by going down on one knee if the answer's still no," he

knee much to the interest of the entire café.

"Marry me, Liz? I can't tell you how much I love you. Please say yes."

The woman's words re-played in her head. *Anyone who goes to that much trouble must be crazy about you.*

"Yes," she whispered.

The customers cheered. Tom slipped the ring on her finger and kissed her.

As if from nowhere his grandparents appeared carrying a bottle of fizz and four glasses! The curse had been broken. Ⓜ

MY INSPIRATION

Words are so powerful; they can't be unsaid and can have a huge positive or negative impact on those around you. As Thumper said in *Bambi*, "If you can't say anything nice, don't say nothing at all."

✦ Their essential basic crop was corn, but they also grew tomatoes, squash, beans, potatoes, avocados and chilli peppers.

✦ The name Aztec comes from the Nahuatl language spoken by the Aztec people, meaning people of Aztlan, a mythical place from where all the Aztecs originated.

✦ The Aztecs were originally a nomadic tribe, believed to have migrated to the south from northern Mexico around 1323, where they settled by a big lake.

✦ They drained the swampy land and created a big artificial island at one end of the lake, which became the capital, called Tenochtitlan.

✦ The Aztecs' native language was Nahuati, which had no alphabet and relied on pictorial sketches.

✦ In 1376, they elected a leader called Acamapichtli, and the Aztec empire formally began.

✦ It is believed that most Aztecs knew how to write Nahuati, but that most of the writing was done by their priests.

FANCY THAT!

Fascinating facts on **The Amazing Aztecs!**

✦ In 1440, Moctezuma I was elected to the throne and he and his descendants expanded the Aztec empire such that by the 1500s they had overthrown most regional kingdoms.

✦ Aztecs also hunted for food as well as farming it. Common animals hunted by them were wild turkeys, rabbits and snakes.

✦ The Aztecs are most known for their love of chocolate, and in fact kingdoms under the rule of Aztecs had to pay cocoa beans as a royalty, or kind of tax, to the king.

✦ The Tonalpohualli was their ritual calendar which determined when the different gods had to be worshipped and when their various festivals would be held.

✦ The ancient Aztecs also cultivated vanilla which was very popular with them and used to flavour their chocolate drinks.

✦ The Aztecs worshipped three dozen or more gods – they had a god for almost anything, including gambling!

✦ The Aztecs built little islands in the lake to serve as farms, each bordered by narrow canals to provide water for crops and as a means to reach the farms by small canoes.

They would mix cocoa beans with water to create a frothy after dinner drink, flavoured with honey, chili or flowers

Gulliver's Travels

Who would have dreamed that a new pet could bring so much joy into a resolutely single girl's life?

By Carrie Hewlett

"You need to get a dog."

Lucy stared at her mum in surprise. "But I've got a cat, why would I get a dog?"

"It would get you out more. Tea?" Her mother busied herself by flicking the kettle switch.

"Yes, thanks. But…why would I want to get out more?" Lucy was sure she was still standing there with her mouth open.

"Well, you've had no-one special in your life since you and Mark split up nearly a year ago. If you had a dog, then you'd have to get out to walk it and then you might meet someone nice."

Lucy rolled her eyes. Trust her mum to be thinking about her love life! She'd lost count of the number of times her mum

Her mum seemed to intuit that she'd hit a nerve as the conversation changed to lighter matters as they sipped their tea.

Curled up on her couch later, Lucy stroked her cat, Mitzi, who purred contentedly like a little traction engine. Instead of her eyes changing into the more usual greenish gold, she still had the most beautiful sapphire blue eyes, eyes that seemed to stare sometimes with such intensity that Lucy was sure they could look into her soul.

Crazy to say, really. But then again animals were perceptive, sensing when something was wrong and offering support the best way they knew how.

Certainly, she'd been glad to have Mitzi curl up on her lap as comfort after she and Mark had had a blazing row and she'd told him to leave. He'd even had

Animals were perceptive, sensing when something was wrong, offering support

had said that by the time she reached the age of twenty-seven, she was married with a baby on the way.

Yes, it was true that she'd not dated anyone since she'd discovered Mark was cheating on her. It still hurt as she'd fallen in love with him early on in their relationship and thought he felt the same. But obviously not.

the audacity to suggest she get rid of her feline friend about seven months after they'd started dating as he didn't like pet fur everywhere.

"But I vacuum daily," she'd said, not wanting to choose between whom she thought the love of her life and the unconditional love only an animal could offer. Although, granted, with cats that

did tend to relate more to being fed and getting attention!

"Your choice of course," Mark had said in a tone that indicated he hoped she'd change her mind.

However, she'd stood firm.

"Love me, love my cat."

Thinking back that had probably been the beginning of the end. And he would have certainly hated it if she'd had a dog as well.

She'd never given much thought to having a pet until one of her friend's cats had kittens. Going round to see them she'd been unable to resist the black and white fur ball that had launched itself against her legs, sniffing her trainers and playing with the laces. Mitzi had come home with her as soon as she was old enough to leave her mother's side.

Climbing into bed, Lucy pondered her mother's suggestion. Was a dog a good idea? After all, didn't cats and dogs fight? And it was quite a responsibility taking on another pet, especially a dog.

On the other hand, living round the corner from the medical centre where she worked, she could pop home regularly to check on it.

She yawned, cuddling down under the duvet, deciding that she'd look into ➡

the practicalities and cost, as perhaps her mum had a point. Not from a romance point of view, but for added companionship. Anyway, dogs were completely loyal – unlike men!

It seemed like fate the following week when she overheard Andrew, one of the nurse practitioners at work, mention that his mum was having problems homing the last of her dog Poppy's puppies. The last pup had a slight kink in his tail.

"She'd like to keep him, but he's full of mischief and with two other dogs as well, she feels she's got enough on her plate."

"Umm, I was thinking of getting a dog. What sort is he?" Lucy asked.

Andrew gave her a warm smile.

"A golden retriever. Six months old

him; this was if Andrew's mum thought her suitable. After all, she was sure that owners vetted people carefully.

With Andrew and herself finishing work at about the same time, he caught up with her as she was pulling on her coat.

"Perfect timing."

Following him in her car, they soon pulled up at a semi-detached property.

"I rang Mum earlier and she's pleased I might have found someone interested," Andrew said.

Leading her towards a front door it opened to reveal a homely-looking woman with eyes as friendly as Andrews. Lucy could hear frantic barking, and the woman smiled as she yelled over her shoulder.

"Ok, you lot. It's only Andrew and a

"I'm just trying to find out how many people Gulliver might be living with..."

now, and fully toilet trained, don't worry."

Seeing the uncertainty on Lucy's face he added quickly, "I'm popping in to see Mum later. Why don't you come along and see him for yourself? If he's not for you, fair enough."

"OK, I will."

Funny. She'd never noticed his brown eyes before. Maybe because she'd been so happy, or so she thought, with Mark. But Andrew's eyes reminded her of liquid gold, as warm as polished amber. Nice.

A frisson of excitement bubbled up inside until she thought of Mitzi. Would she object? She'd heard that cats and dogs could learn to tolerate each other, sometimes even forming a loving bond.

Shaking off any doubts, Lucy created a delightful picture in her mind's eye of Mitzi curled up at the dog's feet with them being the best of friends. Hopefully if she liked the dog, she could afford

nice young woman." She looked at Lucy.

"Do come in, I've got the kettle on. Ignore the mess, with dogs it's all about love rather than having a show home."

Lucy smiled back, soon finding herself surrounded by two larger golden retrievers, before a smaller bundle of golden fur scampered towards her anxious to introduce himself.

"Ohh, you're gorgeous," Lucy cried, crouching down and laughing as a wet nose was pushed towards her.

Andrew's mum looked on approvingly.

"They make loyal family companions. Do you have any children, Lucy?"

"No. But I'd love to one day."

"Boyfriend?"

"Mum!" Andrew admonished.

"Hey, I'm just trying to find out how many people Gulliver might be living with, if Lucy decides she wants him," his mum replied innocently.

"Gulliver?" Andrew looked surprised. "I didn't know you'd named him."

"Well, it's not set in stone but seemed apt as he's adventurous and likes to push boundaries."

"Just like you then," Andrew said affectionately, putting his arm around his mother. "Still seems a bit of an impertinent question to ask though."

"It's OK," Lucy said, chuckling at the mother-son banter. "I was with someone but…well, it didn't work out. Now, it's just me and my cat, Mitzi."

"A cat?"

"Is that OK?" Lucy glanced quickly from mother to son. "She's fairly laid back, and the garden's a good size and fenced in."

After a brief pause, Andrew's mum nodded. "Yeah. This one's friendly enough. Animals have an uncanny knack of knowing whether they should be with someone or not, and Gulliver seems to have taken a real liking to you."

"He's adorable," Lucy said. "And I think Gulliver's a great name."

"See." Mrs Marchant gave her son a knowing look. "Would it be all right if Andrew pops in now and then to see how this little fellow's doing? I'll miss him."

"That's fine," Lucy assured her. After all Andrew seemed like a nice bloke. Agreeing terms, Lucy agreed to sort out the logistics of what she'd need for Gulliver before picking him up the following week.

B ringing Gulliver home for the first time, Lucy practically held her breath. Would the animals take to each other? Mitzi was nowhere in sight. Maybe the cat had sensed something was up?

Gulliver turned his head to look at her as if to say, *is this home?* He then bounded round the garden, sniffing everything, before deciding it was OK, and cocking his leg, making Lucy burst out laughing.

That was before Mitzi appeared, stalking down the garden as though she owned the place, her tail held high in the air, her blue eyes glaring at the intruder. Gulliver immediately growled before slinking back behind Lucy's legs.

"Come on you two," Lucy said encouragingly. "Please be nice to each other."

Mitzi's tail swished as she eyed Gulliver who deciding that it was up to him to make the first move, inched his way out warily from behind Lucy's legs.

"That's it. Go say hello," Lucy said keeping her fingers crossed.

Edging forward, Gulliver stopped several paces from Mitzi before settling on his haunches as if in submission, and wagging his tail as if in greeting. In answer, Mitzi idly lifted one paw to lick clean.

Lucy let out a sigh. OK. First contact had been made. Hopefully, as they got used to each other, relations would become more friendly.

W ith Andrew asking after Gulliver whenever they bumped into each other at work, Lucy decided to ask him round. "If you're free tomorrow night, I can rustle up a bite to eat, then we can take him for a walk."

Andrew grinned.

"Thanks, that sounds great."

Opening the door to him Lucy couldn't stop herself laughing as Gulliver threw ➜

himself at Andrew like a small fireball. "Sorry. I'm trying to train him, but he does seem to have a mind of his own!"

Andrew chuckled. "It's OK. Having grown up with dogs, I'm used to it. If you ever want help in training him, though, just let me know."

"Oh, would you? That would be great as he already knows you. I was going to look into courses."

"No worries.

"We could make a start tonight if you like?"

"Perfect."

With Andrew popping round regularly Lucy began to look forward to the training sessions and seeing him away from work.

His warm brown eyes were as soulful and fun-loving as Gulliver's – and he smelled better! His cologne left a warm, citrus aroma in the air. But being a work colleague, and now a friend, she didn't want to sour things so tried to keep their relationship affable. Not that it was easy to keep a lid on her growing attraction towards him –despite her wariness at trusting another man.

Gulliver seemed to enjoy his training sessions, Andrew having a natural talent in getting the best out of him.

"That's the thing with retrievers, they get bored easily – a bit like small children," he explained.

"I noticed." Lucy grinned. "I've lost count of the new toys I've bought only for him to lose interest. Thankfully he

and Mitzi are getting on OK. She was distrustful initially, but now they seem happy to lie side by side. In fact, there's barely room on the sofa for me now!"

Andrew laughed. "That's dogs for you! You'll just have to sit on my lap when I come round…" His face coloured as he realised what he'd said and he suddenly looked embarrassed. "Sorry… I mean… well, you know."

The air seemed to flash with unspoken feeling between them. Did Andrew feel the same way as Lucy? But how could she be certain she could trust him not to break her heart too? Surely it would be better to just stay friends?

The moment vanished as both Mitzi and Gulliver made an appearance; Mitzi winding herself around Lucy's legs, while Gulliver bounded at Andrew's feet.

"Fine, let's get your lead," Lucy said, noticing that Gulliver made no attempt to hide his love for the dark-haired man at her side. If Mitzi and Gulliver trusted Andrew, could she?

Striding out across the common, the conversation started to flow naturally again. Funny how effortlessly Andrew had settled into her life, Lucy thought. As easily as Mitzi, and Gulliver. Banter flowed between them as comfortably as a river down a valley.

Letting Gulliver run free now that they knew he'd obey her commands, she and Andrew chatted about work or lighter topics; Lucy already knowing that he shared her taste as her in music and films.

They were chatting about the latest Sunday night drama they were both watching when Lucy suddenly looked round and frowned.

"Where's Gulliver gone?"

"He was here a moment ago."

Lucy's heart began to beat furiously,

and she anxiously dragged a hand through her hair. "Gulliver! GULLIVER!"

Together they quickened their pace, running across the field calling Gulliver's name. Then without warning Lucy tripped over a tree root, and would have landed face down in the muddy field if strong arms hadn't caught her.

"You OK?" Andrew's voice sounded full of concern.

"Yes, I…" Out of the corner of her eye she saw Gulliver bounding towards them without a care in the world. "Gulliver!"

Andrew turned his head and smiled.

"I knew he couldn't have gone far," he said before glancing back at Lucy and brushing a stray bit of twig out of her hair.

Gazing up at him, Lucy felt sure she didn't mistake the look in his eyes, even

"After Mark, I found it hard to trust again," she confessed.

"I would never hurt you," Andrew said softly. Staring at him, and seeing the honest reflection in his eyes, Lucy slowly nodded, feeling her heart loosen from the chains she'd wrapped around it.

"Maybe we can be friends as well as…" Andrew let the rest of the sentence hang, though Lucy knew what he meant and felt the blood rush to her cheeks as he kissed her again, this time more passionately.

Cuddling up on Andrew's lap later on the sofa, the rest of the space being taken up by Mitzi and Gulliver, Lucy felt as though life couldn't be more perfect.

Who knew that getting a dog could bring so much joy?

Together they quickened their pace, anxiously calling out Gulliver's name

more so when his head bowed and his lips gently touched hers.

Pulling away they stared at each other, Lucy feeling her heart pound and her pulse race. Though this time it wasn't due to anxiety.

A joyful bark brought her back to her senses and she turned her head to look at Gulliver, who was gazing with adoration at the pair of them as though happy that they'd finally got their act together.

"Do you think he planned it?" Lucy asked, unable to stop herself grinning as she re-attached Gulliver's lead.

"Who knows?" Andrew shrugged before a smile tugged his mouth. "I didn't plan to kiss you just then but somehow it felt right. And, being honest, I've been wanting to for ages, but you were with somebody, and then I didn't want to ruin our friendship."

Though, thinking back, maybe her mum did…

Yes, Lucy thought contentedly, looking at her blue-eyed cat and her adorable brown-eyed golden retriever, it wasn't just cats and dogs who were able to form a loving bond, humans could too. You just had to meet the right one. And yes, it was early days, but just like animals could be a good judge of character and sense when people were meant to be together, sometimes humans had that trait as well – it just took them a while to catch on. Ⓜ

MY INSPIRATION

Anything – from something funny someone says to people watching or bygone memories. One idea can spark off another, and once I start writing my imagination runs away with me.

Dundee Cake

Ingredients

(Makes 1 x 20cm cake)

410 Calories per 100g

- ◆ **175g currants**
- ◆ **325g sultanas**
- ◆ **125g mixed peel**
- ◆ **50g blanched almonds, chopped**
- ◆ **Grated zest 1 large orange**
- ◆ **275g plain flour**
- ◆ **250g butter, cut into pieces**
- ◆ **250g light brown soft sugar**
- ◆ **4 eggs**
- ◆ **2tbsp Seville orange marmalade**
- ◆ **About 65g whole blanched almonds, to decorate**

1 Grease and line a 20cm deep loose-based cake tin. Preheat the oven to 170°C/Fan 150°C/ Gas 3. Combine the currants, sultanas, peel, almonds and orange zest in a bowl. Add half the flour and stir together thoroughly.

2 Place the butter and sugar in a large bowl and beat together until light and fluffy. Gradually beat in the eggs. Fold in the remaining flour, then the fruit, nut and flour mixture. Finally stir in the marmalade.

3 Spoon into the prepared tin and make a slight hollow in the centre of the cake with the spoon. Place the whole almonds, in circles, on top of the cake. Bake for 2hrs, or until a skewer inserted in the centre comes out clean. If necessary, cover the top with foil towards the end of cooking.

4 Leave to cool in the tin. Remove, wrap in greaseproof paper and foil, and store in an airtight container. Leave to mature for at least a week. Use within 6 weeks.

➜ **103**

The House Where Dreams Are Made

After so many years of planning and hoping, could Marguerite's ambition be about to be realised?

By Ellie Holmes

Marguerite watched as the lawyer unscrewed the cap of his fountain pen and laid it to one side. Her world was contained in the pages laid out in front of him. They looked so fragile. She held her breath.

"London?" Her friends had exclaimed when first she had told them of her plans. "Why leave Paris to go there? You're a woman of means now, Marguerite. You could go anywhere."

"Why would you not wish to go to London?" Marguerite had replied with a lift of her head.

How to get across the passion she felt for favourite, Petticoat Lane. So much wonder. So much opportunity.

Rain hit the dusty windowpane and brought Marguerite back to the lawyer's office. The room was cramped with four adults held within, but all was quiet except for the rain and the occasional scratch of the nib of the fountain pen as it moved across the heavy weave of the legal document.

Marguerite watched transfixed as the flowing copperplate lettering recorded her change in status. When the formalities were done, she would own her own property. And not just any property, but a three-storey house; a house where dreams could be made. Not just a home but, most precious of all, a place for her to work.

The passion she felt for her father's home town – the history, the names

her father's home town? The thrill of staring up at the towering buildings, so much history contained within them. The twisted, winding back alleys where sometimes, arms outstretched, she could touch the buildings on either side. Not to mention the wonderfully descriptive names: Cloth Street, Threadneedle Street and her particular

All that had happened had led to this moment: her English father, lost in the Great War, the suspension of her dreams so that she might do her duty and nurse her heartbroken mother through her final illness, the yearning and passion to do something with her life. All of these things had delivered her here to this cramped ➔

solicitor's office in High Holborn. A million miles from Paris, or so it seemed.

Beside her she heard her landlord, Reg, shift in his seat. She looked at him and smiled. He and his wife Rose were perched stiffly on the edge of their wooden chairs, both dressed in their Sunday best, in his case a three-piece woollen suit giving him a florid look in the stuffy room. Rose wore a faded floral dress and a single row of pearls.

"Can't go to a lawyer's office and not get dressed up," Rose had said firmly. "Wouldn't be right."

Marguerite looked down at the red shoes she had arrived in London wearing and the last dress she had made, sewing at her mother's bedside by candlelight, night after night. It had a midnight blue background and was covered in sprays of red and blue flowers.

Marguerite sat once more, demurely folding her hands when all she wanted to do was scream and dance with delight.

The lawyer turned the document and carefully blotted the ink of her signature to prevent runs or smudges.

"You are now the proud owner of a property in London," he declared.

"Very proud," she responded, her voice hardly rising above a whisper.

She watched as the lawyer applied hot wax to the ends of the ribbon which tied the pages of the document together and then pressed his seal into it, leaving the mark of his legal practice within. Then, from his drawer, he lifted out a set of keys on a silver ring.

"These are yours, Miss. I wish you well."

"Merci beaucoup."

Marguerite clutched the keys to her heart. *Thank you, Mama.*

She thought back over the conversation; his smile, the things left unsaid, perhaps

The outfit gave her confidence although she had come to appreciate the red shoes were perhaps a little daring for more conservative English tastes. Certainly, Reg and Rose's eyes had almost popped out of their heads at the sight of them, as had the lawyer's.

The pen stopped moving. Marguerite held herself tense.

"If you would care to sign here."

She lifted her head.

The lawyer pointed a carefully manicured finger towards a spot on the paper.

Taking the pen that was offered, Marguerite stood, praying that her hand would not shake. She wasn't sure why, but it seemed more fitting to sign the document standing up. Then, with a flourish, it was done.

The next day Reg and Rose's son, Joseph, helped Marguerite to move her belongings into the new house. A delivery driver with a local furniture firm, he had been able to borrow the van for a couple of hours.

Now as they carried across the threshold the last of the bits and pieces of furniture Marguerite had been busy collecting during her time in London, she met Joseph's gaze.

"You really did it," Joseph said.

She smiled. "I really did."

"Three storeys? It's a lot of space to fill, mind you."

Marguerite nodded. "The shop will take up all of the ground floor, the workshop and storage area the floor above and my living quarters will be above that. It's not so much space really."

Joseph's expression told her he thought otherwise.

"Dad said he would stop by after work, and we'll move the bigger stuff upstairs."

"Magnifique." Marguerite fanned her hands out over her heart. "That is very kind of you. How blessed I have been to meet such a wonderful family."

She watched the colour lift into Joseph's cheeks.

"Happy to help," he mumbled.

It was only later, when Marguerite was making herself a simple meal in her new home, that she thought back over the conversation with Joseph; the smile, his turn of phrase, the look on his face. The things left unsaid, perhaps?

Was it possible that he had developed feelings for her? Had she been unbelievably dense these last few weeks? Had she missed the signs?

She had never been very good at relationships. She spoke her mind too easily, was too open in the expression of her feelings, both good and bad. One ex-suitor had called her "a very modern woman. Too modern for me."

Bruised, she had retreated into her work. The dresses she made were extensions of herself, the fabric she conjured them from and the equipment she used, her friends. To lose herself for hours in the simple pleasure of making something pretty or practical brought peace and joy to her heart and a quietness to her mind.

Almost unthinkingly, she had gravitated down the stairs to the middle floor of the house. Here was the engine room of her new business. This was where she would sew into the early hours, losing herself in a milieu of chiffons and silks, sequins and pearls.

Her hand came to rest on the blue suitcase she had brought with her from Paris. The brown leather corners were battered and weathered, but she loved every dent and scuff, for held within was the altar at which she would worship hour after hour to create her dreams. Inside was her trusty sewing machine.

For sure, there were bigger and more expensive machines. Hers was a modest, some might say old-fashioned, model. Marguerite did not care. The machine had been a gift from her mama and with it, she knew she could weave magic.

A knock at the front door lifted Marguerite from her thoughts. On ➡

the threshold she found a man in paint-spattered overalls.

"Jenkins, the sign-writer, Miss."

Marguerite smiled.

"I'm pleased to meet you. I need a sign above my new shop."

He nodded. "Your shop, Miss?"

She saw the hook of his eyebrow, the twitch to his lips.

He would be one of those men who naturally assumed a man had bought this shop for her, that she was not capable of supporting herself.

No matter; if he could paint a good sign, that was all she required.

"I want the number 47 to the right of the sign and in the centre a capital M in silver with swirls on the feet of the letter

the counter at the back of the shop.

"But you had no need to buy me a present, Joseph," she chided him gently.

Marguerite stole a look at him as she began to peel back the tape that sealed the box. He stood watching her, a grin on his face, his cap turning nervously in his hands. He liked her; she was sure of it. How could she not have noticed this before? Butterfly wings beat in her stomach at the thought.

She folded back the flaps of the box. Inside was what looked like a metal bracket, and beneath it a smaller box. She lifted out the bracket and as she did so, a bell rang. She laughed in surprise.

"It's a bell to go above the door. As a customer comes in, the bell will ring

How had she not noticed? Butterfly wings beat in her stomach at the thought

and a handful of stars against a midnight blue background. Not too many stars. Not too big. I want them to look…"

She searched for the right word, her English momentarily letting her down.

"Classy. She wants them to look classy."

Marguerite looked up to find Joseph walking towards them carrying a box. She smiled at him.

"Mais oui! Classy," she said.

"Right you are, Miss," the sign-writer said. "I'll start work in the morning."

"Merci, Joseph. Classy is the perfect word," she told him.

He grinned.

"I did not expect to see you until this evening with your father." Her gaze fell to the box in his hands.

"I have half an hour for lunch. Thought I would bring you your present."

"My present?"

"For your new house."

He carefully placed the box on top of

so if you happen to be working upstairs you will still hear it."

"Joseph – how wonderful!"

"And…" He picked up the smaller box and handed it to her, taking the bracket from her hands as he did so.

Inside this box was a small, round bell of the same type she had seen on hotel reception desks.

"If for some reason you don't hear the doorbell, they can approach the counter and ring this one instead. You will surely hear one or the other."

Marguerite watched as he pressed his hand down and the bell rang with such clarity, she clapped her hands in delight.

"I think it should sit here on the edge of the countertop. Ready and waiting for your first customer," he said. "Your first of many," he added.

Marguerite smiled. She knew it was not seemly for a woman to be over-ambitious and yet his words spoke to her heart.

"Tell me, Joseph, what is your mama's favourite colour?"

"Yellow, I think. Why?"

"I want to make her a new dress and there will be new white shirts for both you and your father for all the help you have given me."

"There is no need…"

"Need? Perhaps not," she said. "But still, I shall do it to show my gratitude to you all, non?"

The next four weeks at Number 47 passed in a whirlwind of activity. First, the shop was fitted out with tailor's dummies to model the dresses Marguerite had already prepared. Next came a table and chairs at which she could sit with her customers to go through pattern books and sketches and swatches of material.

Then came the window displays. The bow windows with bottle glass lent themselves perfectly to being staged with Parisian mannequins dressed in her best outfits while above them, her new shop sign dazzled and shone.

The second floor was next. Bolts of material in all of the colours of the rainbow slotted neatly into a stand Joseph had made for her in his free time. Beside them, carefully arranged in a horseshoe shape to take advantage of the light

which poured through the two large sash windows, were three desks. Her trusty sewing machine had pride of place on the middle desk.

"Why three desks?" Joseph had asked.

"One day I shall need help, non? To fulfil all of my orders."

"Of course you will."

"Are you teasing me, Joseph?"

"Teasing? No! It would be a braver man than me who'd bet against you, Marguerite." He had grinned warmly at her.

It was only once the working areas were up and running that Marguerite had turned her attention to the living quarters. A bed, table and chair had sufficed until now. She already knew she would not be spending much time there; her heart would always be in the floors below, but a little more comfort and colour was needed, nonetheless. She swiftly took possession of two armchairs and a sofa. They were plain but Marguerite knew she could fashion new covers for them without too much work. A bookcase, occasional tables and two colourful rugs helped to complete the look and make the upper floor a little more homely.

The furniture, purchased from Joseph's place of work, had earned him a bonus afternoon off which he had promptly pledged to spend with her.

They had taken a walk followed by tea at Lyon's Corner House Teashop on Coventry Street.

There had been several such excursions since. Joseph had delighted in sharing his London with her and as they had walked, he would encourage her to speak of her hopes ➔

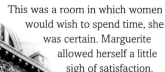

and dreams for the shop without fear of censure or ridicule.

Marguerite knew then that it was not just her dreams that were taking flight at Number 47, her heart was too. When she had least expected it she had found someone who did not seem threatened by her personality or her craving for success. Someone, instead, who

This was a room in which women would wish to spend time, she was certain. Marguerite allowed herself a little sigh of satisfaction. She had held this vision in her mind's eye for so many years and now, finally, it had been realised.

Joseph stood by the front door. "Ready?" he asked. She nodded. "I am." He touched her shoulder,

A companionable squeeze of her shoulder conveyed more than words ever could

seemed to thrive on her passion and rejoice in it. A man who wished to support her not in any financial sense but in the only sense that mattered – by taking an interest, by caring.

When the world had taken from her the two people she had valued most, her mother and father, she had not thought it possible for her battered heart to fly once more. And yet when Joseph was by her side, it did.

Now, as she stood contemplating the shop, a smile bloomed on her face. In stark contrast to the upper floors, the latest in fashionable wallpaper had been applied to the walls of the shop. The table stood ready to welcome visitors with pattern books laid out for perusal, and mannequins flanked the shop floor showing off the best of this season's creations. Vases of fresh flowers gave the room a pleasing scent and a red velvet chaise longue added just the right amount of colour and style.

giving it a companionable squeeze, which conveyed more than words ever could. Then he turned over the sign declaring the shop to be open.

In a short space of time, number 47 had become everything Marguerite had wished it to be: her house, her home, her place of work, her soul – and within it, she had found a sweetheart with whom to share it all.

Her first customer was waiting on the doorstep. Marguerite greeted her with a smile. Over her shoulder, she saw Joseph give her a broad wink.

"Welcome, madame, to the House of Marguerite," she announced. "The house where dreams are made." (MW)

MY INSPIRATION

The scenery, legends and mists of the county of Cornwall and the rugged beauty of Polperro, in particular, are a constant source of inspiration to me.

Brain Boosters

Missing Link

The answer to each clue is a word which has a link with each of the three words listed. This word may come at the end (eg **HEAD** linked with **BEACH, BIG, HAMMER**), at the beginning (eg **BLACK** linked with **BEAUTY, BOARD** and **JACK**) or a mixture of the two (eg **STONE** linked with **HAIL, LIME** and **WALL**).

ACROSS

7 Celebrity, Column, Hot (6)
8 Good, Oddly, Well (6)
9 Blocker, Particle, Rhythm (4)
10 Dental, Fee, Old (8)
11 Army, Instinct, Waters (11)
14 Form, Job, Software (11)
18 Dioxide, Gas, Liquid (8)
19 Air, Out, Road (4)
20 Boot, Island, Sahara (6)
21 Liquid, Mask, Tent (6)

DOWN

1 Battery, High, Solar (7)
2 Central, Minor, Pacific (4)
3 Free, Level, White (6)
4 Private, Public, Third (6)
5 Chord, Gene, Male (8)
6 Fully, To, With (5)
12 Cub, News, War (8)
13 Beer, Motorcycle, Ski (7)
15 Bright, Fairy, Foot (6)
16 Ball, Fodder, Loose (6)
17 Guide, Side, Sight (5)
19 Alpha, Electric, Sting (4)

Turn To Page 157 For Solutions

Hidden word in the shaded squares: _____

A Journey Back In Time

A chance connection at a celebration forty years earlier had led them here… so what would they discover?

By Lisa Allen

The car slowed to a stop outside the tall, rusty, wrought iron gates and for a moment, Alice couldn't speak. Dark trees flanked either side like guards protecting a fortress. Tumbledown pillars and a crumbling wall stretched along the lost country road, and in the distance creeping ivy wound its heart-shaped hands around a grand but weary house, as if set on holding it back in time.

"Are you sure this is the place?" James glanced uncertainly at his wife, engine still quietly running, hands on the wheel.

Alice wound down the window and a rush of warm air scented the car with wild flowers and grasses, pine trees and mystery. She just about made out the

Eight hours earlier

"Have we got everything?"

James raised an eyebrow, squeezing the car boot shut over a pile of suitcases.

"Everything except the kitchen sink."

Alice grinned, excitement bubbling in her chest; this was their first proper long road trip as a family. Usually their holiday was a quick flight to Spain. Days spent lazing by the pool surrounded by inflatable sharks and unicorns, endless noise, and a free bar.

Not that she didn't love that – especially the free bar – but sometimes it was nice to have a change. And this year couldn't get much more different, because two things had happened.

First, was the much anticipated arrival of Ted; a clever little terrier who loved

"This is it," she said. The enormity of what she'd agreed to was taking hold

house address through the layers of lichen covering a gate plaque.

"This is it," said Alice, sounding calmer than she felt. The enormity of what she'd agreed to do was taking hold. Reflected in the wing mirror, Alice caught the disappointed looks of her children's faces, and a pang of mum-guilt pulled at her heart.

What was she thinking – bringing her family here for their holiday?

being the centre of his adoring family's attention (Alice, James, teenage Noah, and eight-year-old Lucie). Ted's most recent trick unfortunately involved destroying their lovely back garden, or as Lucie called it, 'digging for treasure'. Alice, however, was yet to find the value in a cheesy old trainer.

Second though, was sad news; Alice received an official and rather upsetting ➤

letter in the post, sent from Yorke & Austin, solicitors.

Dear Alice,

We are writing on behalf of our late client, Miss Ginny Dibden… a distant relative… We have been instructed… obliged if you could assist… sadly a state of disrepair… profits of the house sale to be distributed between charities… personal items she wished you to have… Our sincere condolences.

Alice remembered Ginny immediately. London, the 1980s. It was Alice's great-aunt's fiftieth birthday party.

Electro-pop music beat across the dance floor and tropical lights spun over tight perms and neon outfits.

Alice wanted to be dancing too, but she didn't recognise the few children her age at the party, among all the adults her mum seemed to know.

"You should show off what you've been learning at your Disco Dancing classes, Alice," her mum cajoled.

Alice shook her head. She didn't want to on her own.

Her mum smiled at the woman seated nearby. They'd been chatting for a while and it turned out were distantly related. Ginny, who had spiky hair, even spikier

Dancing next to Ginny, Alice felt like one of the stars of her favourite Friday night music show. And that one simple act of kindness had stayed in Alice's heart.

Alice wiped a tear from her cheek. To think, Ginny had remembered Alice after all these years. Alice was now, the letter stated, her closest living relative. She wanted Alice to choose some personal things from her house, and the solicitors politely asked if perhaps Alice could stay at the house the week before its sale to get it presentable – the money would be going to Ginny's chosen charities.

Alice replied immediately, agreeing to their request. Unfortunately, the arrangements coincided with school holidays. The family had already agreed on a staycation because of Ted.

But they'd booked a seaside lodge; plenty of walks for Ted, beach and pier amusements, and dog-friendly tourist attractions for entertainment – a week of non-stop family fun. So it had taken a little persuasion on Alice's part to convince her family to cancel it for what would essentially be a working family holiday.

It's like a museum in here," groaned Noah, adjusting his headphones, angry metal music faintly thrashing around his unimpressed expression.

On cue, her husband's hand shot to his hip, the other launching like an arrow

shoulder pads and a pretty sparkling brooch, gave Alice a bright smile. Alice thought she looked like a film star.

"I'd love to dance, but I've got two left feet," Ginny said, pretending to look embarrassed. "I don't suppose you could show me some disco moves, Alice?"

Alice nodded, suddenly excited as they shimmied across the ballroom.

"Don't touch anything," quipped James, trying to lighten the mood.

"Mummy, I don't like it," complained Lucie, clinging to Alice's hand as they wandered through the dark, musty-smelling rooms, Ted tip-tapping inquisitively behind. "It's scary."

"Bet there are vampires and bats here at night," teased Noah meanly, causing

his little sister to cry out, "Mummy!"

"Noah!" snapped Alice. The house worryingly appeared to need a lot more work than she'd envisaged. Was this about to become the worst holiday ever?

James put a reassuring hand on her shoulder.

"It looks worse than it is," he said, his ability to read her thoughts as uncannily strong as when they'd first met. "Once we get all the curtains and windows opened, things will seem brighter."

O ver the next few days, the family swirled about the house like a giant octopus; a mop and duster in each hand, tentacles swishing up and down, over and round, dust clouds like billows of sand swirling up from the sea bed floor.

It was fun at first.

Noah found Ginny's old record collection; a musical story of her life played out from 1930s Jazz orchestra, 40s wartime songs, rock and roll of the 50s and 60s, right up to 70s anarchic punk and twenty-first century ballads. The record player crackled as Noah replaced the vinyl again; a 1980s electro-pop classic synthesising into the lounge.

"This is it!" cried Alice, nearly falling off the stepladder. "The first song I danced to with Ginny at my great-aunt's party."

She started recreating the moment.

"Mum," said Noah, grumpily, "you're being embarrassing."

Straight-faced, Alice replied, "Yeah? Well, wait 'til you see this!"

Her arms flailed comically through a spotlight of gold dust motes, an eyebrow arching at James.

On cue, her husband's hand shot to his hip, the other launching like an arrow through the air with rather impressive musical timing.

Lucie burst into giggles, joining in with a jiggle. Not one to be left out, Ted sprang about their ankles, barking to the beat of the drums.

Noah covered his face with his hands; for the first time this week he was glad they were miles from anyone he knew.

Alice reached out her hand.

"Go on, Noah. You can be un-cool just for a couple of minutes, can't you?"

Noah's face broke into a grin. "I'm never un-cool," he said. "Not with these moves." He started busting out the latest dance routine from social media, deliberately making them all fall about with laughter.

O ver the following days, Alice uncovered more and more about Ginny that she might never have known. Diary entries detailed Ginny's relationships and life. She'd worked ➤

as a typist for many years, before a chance encounter in the 1950s led to a brief move to America to pursue a career as an actress. Alice remembered how glamorous Ginny had seemed at her great aunt's party.

A few rolled-up film posters crediting Ginny in supporting roles, and photographs of a younger Ginny in glamorous black and white headshots, were discovered in a box on top of her old armoire. There was even an old typed script, bit-part dialogue underlined in ink.

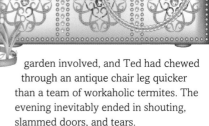

"Mummy, I'm going to be a film star like Ginny when I grow up," said Lucie, staring in wonder at the posters.

Alice smiled. Maybe the aptitude ran in the family. Lucie already attended Saturday morning dance and performance classes with her friends.

As Alice sifted through Ginny's personal items, she opened a dressing table drawer and was hypnotised by a piece of costume jewellery. She recognised the brooch immediately; it was the one Ginny had worn on her dress at the party. Next to it, there was a scribbled message on a scrap of paper:

Alice, I hope this brooch finds you still happy and dancing.

Thank you,

Love always, Ginny

Alice pinned the brooch to her cardigan, staring at her reflection in the dressing table mirror. She could hear music, pictured lights beaming, and as she closed her eyes just for a moment, Alice felt Ginny's smiling face next to hers.

By the end of the week, tiredness had kicked in. Lucie and Noah were bickering non-stop, James was continually moaning about how much work the garden involved, and Ted had chewed through an antique chair leg quicker than a team of workaholic termites. The evening inevitably ended in shouting, slammed doors, and tears.

Alice stared across the moonlit garden. It was covered in shades of night green, still messy and in need of love.

James appeared, wrapping his hand around hers, warming her soul.

"I'm sorry it's not turning out like our usual holidays," Alice said quietly.

James squeezed her hand.

"What on earth are you talking about? The kids are arguing, there's barely been five minutes for just us, and we've spent all week doing chores and looking after everyone. It's been *exactly* like our usual holidays."

Alice burst out laughing. "You always know how to make me feel better."

James smiled.

"Come on, we're doing this for Ginny. In her last wishes she thought of you. You both made an imprint on each other's memories. That's special."

Alice's eyes were filmy. Why hadn't she thought to reconnect with Ginny before it was too late? Or tried to find a phone number to make sure she was OK? She looked up at the stars glittering in the sky. *We'll do our best for you here, Ginny,* she resolved. *You'll always be in my heart. And your kindness will never be forgotten.*

The next morning, as Alice sifted through a box of photographs of Ginny and her friends at various stages of fashion, shrieks and shouts echoed through the open windows.

Alice's shoulders slumped. Not again. When would her children learn to get along? She dropped the photos, following the cries into the garden.

The sun was shining like a gold coin in a sea-blue sky as Lucie jumped up and down on the wooden bench shouting like a pirate. Ted – who had something hanging out of his mouth – was excitedly cannonballing across the garden as Noah emerged from the overgrown muddy grass like a mythical sea beast, trying to catch the lively terrier.

Ted's head spun round at the word "biscuit". He slowed to a stop near Alice.

Grinning, she slipped her hand into her pocket, retrieving two dog biscuits and stretching out her palm.

Ted's nose twitched. Gingerly, he padded closer, lifting his chin so his treasure-find was ever so slightly out of Alice's reach.

She shook her head, defeated.

"Fine. Have it your way, Ted. Three biscuits. And that is my absolute final offer." She jangled the loot in front of him like a bag of money.

Satisfied, Ted opened his mouth and a small metal chest dropped to the ground. A slobbery tongue swept across Alice's palm, Hoovering up the biscuits.

"Eww, Ted!"

She wiped her hand on her jeans and picked up the treasure chest. It was a very old biscuit tin; discoloured and engraved with a pretty design. Curiously, she lifted

He tried to leap in front of Ted, only to be knocked down like a human skittle

"What is going on?" Alice demanded.

"Ted's found treasure!" shrieked Lucie, excitedly joining in the chase.

Alice groaned as a flash of fur skidded past her ankles, spraying her with dirt.

"Not another cheesy old trainer?"

"No," gasped Noah through gulps of laughter. He tried to leap in front of Ted, only to get knocked down like a human skittle again. "It must be valuable, 'cos he won't give it up!"

Alice bit her lip. She shouldn't encourage them, it would be her scrubbing the mud out of Noah's clothes and Ted's fur later, but it was nice to see them all playing nicely again.

"OK, Ted, what's your ransom? One gravy biscuit?"

its lid, her eyes widening with surprise.

Lucie ran over, balancing on her tiptoes to see inside.

"What is it, Mummy?"

Noah slouched towards them, attempting to wipe mud off his hoodie.

"Yeah, Mum, has Ted finally made us millionaires?"

Alice smiled. "I think we'd better take a look at this indoors."

Scratched on the inside of the lid were Ginny's name and the date *1940*. War had broken out, and according to scribed notepapers wrapped around the keepsakes, Ginny stayed on at the house with her grandmother and sisters while her parents joined up to help the ➜

war effort.

At night, we hear the planes roaring overhead. I feel scared in the darkness, but Grandmother says we are not to switch on the lights – the house is hidden to keep us all safe…

Among the keepsakes were a pretty bracelet, a small hand-stitched bear, a poem signed off 'written by Ginny, Mary and Catherine', and two photos – a man in army uniform, and a woman in a nurse's dress, captioned on the back with *Father* and *Mother*.

"Do you think they might have buried

unashamedly dancing and laughing as if there was no one watching. And James, her supportive husband, holding Alice's hand beneath a starry moonlit sky. Thanks to Ginny, they were memories she would cherish forever.

Alice had contacted the solicitors; hopefully the house sale proceeds would make a real difference to Ginny's chosen charities in the future.

Alice hoped Ginny would have been proud of what they'd achieved. This week they'd travelled back in time – it had been a holiday her family would never forget.

Among the keepsakes were a bracelet, a hand-stitched bear and photos

it in the garden as a time capsule?" asked Noah, staring solemnly at the photo of Ginny's father.

"Quite possibly," said James. "They were living through dangerous times. Maybe they were worried their most precious things would be taken."

"Could we keep these?" Noah looked at his parents. "We're doing a history project on the second World War at school next term. I'd really like to include Ginny's records of her experience."

Alice smiled, emotion pressing her chest. "I think that's a lovely idea, Noah."

"I told you Ted really can find treasure," beamed Lucie.

A s the car wound along the dark country roads going home, Alice's memories journeyed through the family's week together. Ted's wagging tail as he teasingly offered up his prize. Lucie's proud declaration of 'Ted really can find treasure!' Noah, moody and too cool,

A few hours later and the car turned onto Norton Street. Alice could see their house lantern glimmering in the night. Theirs was a small terraced house, with small rooms and an equally small garden; nothing like Ginny Dibden's sprawling stone lodge and its surrounding fields.

But it was theirs, and it was cosy, and Alice felt a warm feeling in her heart as the car pulled along the pavement, slowing to a stop.

Alice glanced down at the brooch that was still pinned to her cardigan, and smiled; a beautiful reminder to always be happy, and always be dancing. (MW)

MY INSPIRATION

My stories are inspired by nature and the world around me. I love writing stories which reflect nostalgically on the past as well as looking forward to a brighter future.

✦ Ancient China boasts the longest lasting empire in history. It began with the first emperor Qin who united China under one rule in 221BC, and ended with the Qing dynasty (1644-1912).

✦ The last emperor of China, Puyi, became ruler when he was only 3 years old.

✦ In some parts of ancient China, pigtails indicated a girl's marital status. A young girl would wear two pigtails, and after marriage, she would wear just one.

✦ Toilet paper was invented in China, but it was only made available to Emperors!

✦ The dragon is regarded as a symbol of good fortune. Chinese emperors called themselves dragons' sons, born with power to rule the country.

✦ The antithesis of the dragon is the phoenix, representing feminine power. Both creatures are auspicious in Chinese culture.

FANCY THAT!

Fascinating facts on **Ancient China!**

✦ Chopsticks were first used in China for cooking, not eating. They were invented before the Shang dynasty (1600–1046 BC) and by the time of the Han dynasty (206 BC–220 AD), they were used as eating utensils.

✦ The bicycle was first introduced into China in 1891, and to begin with, it was a luxury item. The last Qing emperor rode a bicycle around the Forbidden City. Today, China is the world leader in bicycle production.

✦ China was the first country in the world to use paper money, printed in 1023 during the Northern Song dynasty, in Sichuan Province.

✦ In Ancient China, boys whose families could afford it were sent to school and once they passed certain tests, they received government grants and their families gained tax-exemption.

✦ Paper was invented in China. Before its invention, the Chinese transcribed characters on tree bark, scrolls, cloth, bronze ware, and bamboo.

✦ Ice cream was invented in China around 200 BC – a frozen mixture of milk, rice, and snow.

✦ By the time Marco Polo arrived in China, around 1270, eyeglasses were widely used in Chinese upper class, and were mentioned in his accounts.

Cricket fighting was a popular pastime in China, and hence many Chinese children kept crickets as pets

The Fourth Musketeer

Carrie could never have guessed what happiness her old car breaking down would bring into her life

By Gill McKinlay

I reckon Hollywood should remake *The Three Musketeers*," Ella said. "Good idea," Bev replied. "I love all that swashbuckling and swordplay. And the musketeers are such a great team."

Carrie sipped her coffee and sighed at the topic of conversation: men. Again.

Divorced last year, she had little time for the opposite sex, famous or otherwise.

"If you were casting for a new version of *The Three Musketeers*, which actors would you choose?" Bev asked.

Names were suggested, and rejected, until the roles were filled.

Well, almost.

partner worked abroad for long stretches.

They'd welcomed Carrie on her first day at PoliciesRus Insurance and now they were both friends and colleagues.

On Saturday evenings, the trio bonded over wine in Bev's lovely garden, catching the last of the summer sunshine, surrounded by bees buzzing in the fragrant lavender and roses.

Cassie loved those evenings. Coming from London, she hadn't known life could be so friendly. After her divorce, she'd left the city for a fresh start and ended up buying a terraced house in the small seaside town of Flintsea – perfect.

As Bev and Ella nominated footballers and F1 racing drivers, young Jamie

Carrie was content alone but sometimes thought it would be nice to feel needed

"That's Porthos, Athos and Aramis sorted," Ella said, "But what about D'Artagnan?"

"You're right, Ella," Bev grinned. "Who do you fancy as the fourth musketeer, then Carrie?"

Carrie suggested some ageing-but-still-sexy rock stars, and a couple of TV personalities, all vetoed by Bev and Ella.

Carrie smiled and let the banter wash over her, happy to be here with her new friends; widowed Bev, and Ella whose

wandered into the lunchtime rest room.

He upended a carrier bag: sandwiches, fizzy drinks and chocolate bars fell on to the table. Then he aimed a foil package at the bin, as he did every day.

Bored with the auditions for D'Artagnan, Carrie frowned at him.

"Why don't you ever beat the sandwiches your mum makes for you?" she asked. "It's such a waste, chucking them out like that."

"My mum doesn't make them." Jamie

ripped open a triangular packet. "She ran off with the window cleaner three years ago. It's just me and dad now."

"Does he make the sandwiches, then?"

"Yes, and they're always cheese and pickle – even the ones from the shops taste better."

"So, why not just ask your dad to stop making them?"

"He'd be upset. He blames himself for Mum walking out and likes to think he's looking after me."

Carrie sighed. Much as she hated to admit it, she could sympathise with Jamie's dad. She'd adjusted to being on her own, but sometimes, she wished she could do something for somebody else.

Carrie hadn't mentioned these feelings to Bev or Ella as they might start matchmaking, pair her up with a member of Bev's extensive family, or one of her many friends.

Ella was a slave to social media and had a lot of mates online, but Bev seemed ➡

to know the life history of everybody living within a ten-mile radius of Flintsea. She'd have Carrie partnered in no time and she didn't want that.

It would be nice to feel needed though, Carrie thought as Jamie opened a can of drink. And she longed to repay the kindness her new friends had shown.

One day, she hoped to invite them to drink wine in her garden. Not yet though. It needed pruning, weeding and mowing.

Bev had told her not to worry.

"My brothers will sort it for you."

She'd already sent round relatives to plumb-in Carrie's white goods, install a new bathroom and do some painting. And Ella, efficient at IT, had set her up on the local Facebook and WhatsApp groups.

"There was nothing like this in London," Carrie said, as she scrolled through a page of community events. Or if there was, she hadn't known about it. That was the trouble with big cities; they teemed with people too busy to talk to each other.

Five o'clock arrived with D'Artagnan

to the extreme, he even parked the souped-up vehicle diagonally across two parking bays so nobody could accidentally prang it when they opened their doors.

How he could afford the insurance baffled Carrie, but then they worked for an insurance company so maybe he'd wrangled a brilliant deal.

"Will you make it home in that heap?" he asked Carrie, elbow resting on the wound-down window. "Or shall I phone the fire brigade?"

"It'll be OK," Carrie replied. "It won't let me down. It never lets me down. Bev's cousin Pete is a mechanic and he's kept it going ever since I moved here."

"If you say so." Jamie sounded doubtful and rightly so…

Ten minutes later, Carrie's car had conked out on the dual carriageway. Pete failed to answer his phone and as no amount of kicking or cursing would start the car, she had to phone for assistance. Waiting for the breakdown truck to arrive, Carrie wondered whether the

After a quick test drive in the gorgeous sleek red convertible, Carrie signed for it!

still not cast. Despite arguing all afternoon, Bev and Ellie just couldn't agree on a leading man.

Pleased to leave the office and feel the sunshine on her skin, Carrie climbed into her battered Ford. After coughing and spluttering, the engine finally wheezed into life.

Just then, Jamie, partially hidden by the cloud of smoke, pulled up in his pride and joy. A present for his twenty-first birthday, he spent most of his salary on expensive accessories for the car, his weekends taken up with extensive cleaning and polishing routines. Obsessive

driver could play D'Artagnan.

"Thank goodness they're not casting a real movie," she'd muttered to Jamie earlier. "It'd never get off the ground."

"Why is the book called *The Three Musketeers* when there are four of them?" he'd asked.

"Try reading it instead of cruising around the seafront in that car of yours," Bev snapped, overhearing the last remark.

"I like cruising – it's fun," Jamie replied, as he'd tried to decipher a handwritten document.

However, as the truck arrived, Carrie knew her knight in shining armour

couldn't play D'Artagnan. Her rescuer was female – Bev and Ella would never consider a woman for the role but perhaps they should…

"Hi." The girl jumped down from the cab. "I'm Zoe."

After faffing under the bonnet with various gadgets and leads, Zoe wandered around the vehicle inspecting it thoroughly.

"It'll cost more to fix than it's worth," Zoe said, bluntly. "Time to scrap it."

Carrie blinked. Get rid of it? No way! She'd kept the car as part of the divorce settlement. Letting it go would mean finally saying goodbye to the past. Although she'd moved away from London and into a lovely, friendly community, she loved her old car. She'd feel lost without it. That it would fizzle out and die, like her marriage, hadn't occurred to her.

Doug reckoned cars had a ten-year life span. After that, it was time for a new model. He'd applied that rule to their marriage and after ten anniversaries, he'd traded Carrie in for something more modern.

"Maybe I should do the same," Cassie thought as she phoned Bev's taxi-driving nephew for a lift home. "Perhaps it's time for a change."

On Saturday, Carrie trawled some car showrooms.

"This is perfect for you." A salesman who looked about fourteen, steered her towards a small grey hatchback. "It's cheap to run, a joy to drive, and very easy to park, too."

Cassie sighed. She was fed-up with models that all looked the same.

"If I'm going to spend a fortune, I might as well have something with a bit of oomph," she muttered.

She pointed to a sleek scarlet red convertible parked in pole position. She had already seen it advertised on the television, it had received rave reviews from all the leading motoring organisations.

"I'd like to test drive that, please."

After driving around the block a few times, Carrie fell in love again and signed on the dotted line… ➔

Once he'd ditched his sandwich, Jamie spent the lunch break on the staff car park drooling over Carrie's car. He asked numerous questions about the spec, none of which she could answer.

"It's just a car," she muttered. "You put petrol in the tank, and it goes…"

"It's more than just a car – it's wicked! Are you up for taking it cruisin'?"

"Cruising?"

"Yeah, you know, when all the flash cars drive along the seafront. It's a sort of parade that happens every Saturday evening during the summer – it's been going on for years."

Carrie frowned. The local newspapers were always banging on about the cruisers and some residents had complained to the police about them. Although the cruisers were careful not to break any rules, she wasn't sure she should get involved.

"Isn't it just for youngsters?"

"It's about the cars not the drivers. And this car deserves mega attention."

"Well, it's a nice idea, but I don't think it's really me. Anyway, I go to Bev's on Saturday evenings. We drink wine in the garden." Carrie wished she was there now, actually.

"Can't you miss it for once? What is it about drinking wine in the garden with those two anyway? You see them every day at work."

"They're my friends," she said. "And it's the little things, like making time for each other, that are important."

"Well, I'm your friend too so you should make some time for me. But you're like my dad – stuck in a rut."

Carrie stared at him. Doug had accused her of being in a rut when she'd refused to go white water rafting to celebrate their 10th wedding anniversary. Looking back, she realised that row marked the end of their relationship. He wanted to do sporty stuff and she just wanted a quiet life. And nothing had changed.

She still avoided sporty adventures, but driving a car was an everyday event. Was she so set in her ways that she couldn't embrace even the simplest of new ideas? What harm could there possibly be in driving a car along the seafront?

"OK," she said. "I'm, er, well up for it. I'll follow you."

Carrie may have been up for it, but when Saturday arrived, Jamie wasn't.

"The exhaust has fallen off," he wailed down the phone. "And I can't get it sorted until Monday."

"No problem," Carrie said, secretly relieved. She could go to Bev's as usual. "We'll go another time."

"No, I've been looking forward to cruisin' all week. We can both ride in your wheels. Pick me up at eight."

Carrie ended the call feeling slightly apprehensive.

However, as she eased her car along the seafront, the dazzling neon lights, screams from the rollercoaster and the shouts and waves from the crowds made Carrie feel young and glad to be alive. She'd never felt such exhilaration in London, or had this much attention, either.

She'd forgotten the smell of vinegar, salt, and chips, warm air, cold beer, and candyfloss. White water rafting seemed tame in comparison.

Jamie found some rap music on the radio, something she'd never listened to before, and chatted to some mates on his mobile called Bro and Dude…

All in all, Carrie had a fun night.

"Cheers, Jamie," she said as she dropped him home. "I've actually really

sometime. Goodnight, Jamie – see you at work on Monday."

Furious, she selected first gear, and headed back towards the seafront. But the magic had gone. Annoyed with Jamie's dad for getting the wrong end of the stick, she didn't notice the big wheel, the water splash, or the illuminations.

How dare he make insinuations? Carrie hoped that Jamie would bin every meal his dad cooked over the weekend. It'd serve him right!

Sighing, she parked outside Bev's hoping her friends were still in the garden. They were.

The temperature had dropped so they were wearing cardigans and there was still some wine in the bottle.

"…and to think I'd sympathised with Jamie's father over the sandwiches,"

He may have jumped to conclusions, but I reckon he'd make a good D'Artagnan

enjoyed this evening."

"I'll bet you have," drawled a male voice. As Jamie got out of the car a man suddenly appeared from behind a hedge. Even with the fading light, Carrie could see that he was tall, dark and handsome.

"Shut up, Dad, you've got it all wrong. Carrie's a mate from work."

Flushed with embarrassment Jamie apologised to Carrie and then tried explaining the situation to his father, but he wouldn't listen.

Despite feeling gooey inside, Carrie glared at the stupid man in front of her. No wonder his wife had run off with the window cleaner! She hoped his windows were streaked with grime!

"There are no rules about friendship," she snapped. "Anyone can be friends with anybody they choose. You should try it

Carrie said, as she updated them.

"But you have to see it from Mike's point of view," Bev said. Trust her to know him! "He worries about Jamie, and he doesn't know you from Eve. He saw his son out with an older woman, put two and two together, and came up with ninety-five! I reckon he'd make a good D'Artgnan, though."

"No, he wouldn't," Ella argued. "Mike is too tall, too dark, and too handsome. Musketeers are always a bit scruffy and dishevelled – in a good way," she added.

Feeling more relaxed, Carrie grinned – had they really been discussing D'Artagnan all night?

Carrie spent Sunday worrying about Jamie – were they still friends? Would there be an awkward atmosphere at ➜

work on Monday? She hoped not.

But she needn't have worried.

Jamie breezed in, late as usual, minus the tinfoil package.

"Me and Dad had a massive row after you'd left," he said, cheerfully. "I told him not to bother with the sandwiches, that I could make them myself."

Later, in reception, a girl handed Carrie a huge bouquet of seasonal blooms – the girl was Bev's niece if Carrie wasn't mistaken.

She found a card among the foliage:

I'm sorry for jumping to conclusions. Can we be friends? How about dinner Saturday evening? Mike x

PS Jamie for D'Artagnan.

He'd added a phone number. So, Jamie really had talked to his dad. He'd even told him about their stupid game, and Mike had sorted the problem!

asked, as Cassie returned to her desk. "Are you going for dinner with Dad?"

"The flowers are beautiful, but I'm going to Bev's on Saturday."

"Meet Dad another evening, then. Please don't turn him down. It's taken him ages to get over Mum leaving."

"A restaurant seems too formal. I'd prefer a picnic." Carrie placed the flowers on her desk and picked up her phone. "We could drive somewhere in my car."

"That's a great idea; he loves your car. I'll make a picnic for you."

Jamie pulled off an imaginary musketeer hat and bowed, "I'm honoured, m'lady"

"Mike has suggested Jamie for the fourth musketeer," she told Bev and Ella as she passed their desks.

"Great! Why didn't we think of that?" Bev asked.

"Jamie's not as tall, dark, or handsome as his dad yet," Ella remarked. "Which makes him perfect for the role. Jamie – you're D'Artagnan," she yelled at him across the office.

Jamie stood up, removed an imaginary hat from his head, and performed a sort of half-bow-half-curtsy.

"I'm honoured, m'lady."

"Thank goodness that's settled," Bev said. "Now, what about a new King Arthur film – who do you fancy for the lead?"

"Do you like the flowers?" Jamie

"You'd do that?"

"I'm D'Artagnan – I can do anything."

"Thanks, that's really sweet of you."

"I mean, just think, if all goes well, we could be family," he went on. "So, you might want to think about adding Dad and me to your car insurance."

"Why?"

Jamie held up his hand for a high-five.

"All for one, and one for all…" Ⓦ

. . . .

MY INSPIRATION

I love green spaces so living close to a park is a blessing. I also enjoy gardening and tending an allotment. These activities bring most pleasure when shared with my grandchildren.

RECIPE AND FOOD STYLING: JENNIE SHAPTER PHOTOGRAPHY: JON WHITAKER

84
Calories per
100g

Spiced Pears

Ingredients
(Makes about 2 kg)

- ◆ **225g golden granulated sugar**
- ◆ **500ml white wine vinegar**
- ◆ **7.5cm piece fresh root ginger, thinly sliced**
- ◆ **1 x 15cm cinnamon stick, broken into 3**
- ◆ **1tsp juniper berries**
- ◆ **1 star anise**
- ◆ **1 lemon, halved**
- ◆ **1.5kg ripe but firm pears**

1 Place the sugar and vinegar in a large saucepan. Add the ginger, cinnamon, juniper berries and star anise. Pare the rind off half the lemon and add with the juice. Slice the remainder. Slowly bring to the boil.

2 Meanwhile peel, halve or quarter and core the pears. Add to the pan with the lemon slices. Simmer gently for 10-15min, or until the pears are just tender.

3 Remove the pears, lemon slices and spices with a slotted spoon and pack in sterilised jars. Bring the syrup to the boil and boil for 10min to reduce by about a third.

4 Pour over the pears, making sure they are completely covered. Seal when cold, label and store in a cool dark place for at least 3 weeks. Use within 6 months.

➜ **119**

Letting The Light In

After the grieving, Alice discovered ways to grow around the pain of loss, ways to step out from the dark…

By Gillian Harvey

A s they rounded the corner, the familiarity of the view made her gasp. It had been three years, yet little had changed in the tiny hamlet. The phone box – a relic, almost, from another time – still standing proud on the grass verge. The houses, dotted here and there in the same pattern they'd formed for the last hundred years or so.

Then slightly further along, the roadway dipped and rose and there it was – the tiny, whitewashed house, blue shutters closed, looking for all intents and purposes exactly as they'd left it.

Alice didn't know exactly why she'd expected things to be different. She'd changed. Yet, for her, everything had.

"I forgot how gorgeous this place was," said Tilly, pulling up outside the wooden gate. "It's so peaceful, isn't it?"

"You used to hate it," said Alice. "Both of you!" She glanced in the mirror, caught Lorna's eye and smiled. "Said it was the most boring place on earth."

"God, we were awful teenagers, weren't we, mum?" Tilly said. "Didn't know a good thing when we saw it."

"No, you were right," said Alice. "It's no place to bring fifteen-year-old girls. No shops, no people to meet…"

"No phone signal," chimed Lorna from the back. "That was the worst bit."

"Oh, god, I hope things have improved since then!" Tilly said, with mock angst.

They smiled, remembering their yearly family holidays to the Cornish cottage

carried on paying the neighbour who'd kindly cut the grass once a fortnight during the summer. She'd known all was well with the cottage; he'd have let her know if there'd been any storm damage or burst pipes.

It was just, seeing the house looking just as it had looked when she and Grahame had locked the door behind them and set off for home three years ago, seemed wrong, because nothing had

They all smiled, remembering the yearly holidays to Cornwall. The twins had been three when Grahame had inherited the cottage from an elderly aunt – twenty years ago now – and they'd raced down the first chance they'd got. It had been empty for a year or more – the aunt had lived in London and had stopped visiting the house as she'd grown frail – and had smelled of mildew – but Grahame had been over the moon. "Beats ➤

camping," he'd declared, as they'd sat outside the French windows, sipping wine in the garden. "Splash of paint, few bits of furniture, and it'll be grand."

The first decade of Cornish holidays had been blissful. Red wellies and nets and rockpools.

Belly boarding and sandcastles. Sand between toes, in hair, falling from socks when you slipped them off at night. They'd arrive home salted and fresh and windswept and tanned, feeling completely revitalised.

As the girls had grown, the holidays had changed shape. They'd spent less time at the beach and more driving to local towns, trying restaurants, taking boat rides, trying to keep two teenagers as happy as possible. Then, at 16, the girls had decided a week without mum and dad at home would give them more of a break than the Cornish wilds ever could, and Alice and Grahame had set off alone.

The drive was four hours, door-to-door, and they'd often break it up with a stop halfway. And after the initial disappointment of the girls' rejection, they'd come to love their breaks at the cottage. Alice had taken up a bit of amateur water-colouring in the evenings and Grahame had become something of a beachcomber, filling his pockets with smooth sea glass, worn wood and other tidal treasures on their many walks.

Now, as they pushed open the gate, Alice felt Tilly's hand on her arm. None of them spoke. She breathed deeply, inhaling the unique smell of grasses and shrubs, the salty hit of the sea beyond. She felt the air filling her lungs, refreshing and revitalising as ever, as familiar as a long-lost friend.

The girls had been right – it had been too long.

They'd first suggested the trip two years ago. A year after the accident that had stolen Grahame from them all.

"Come on mum," Lorna had said. "We can book time off work, go together. It'll be nice."

But Alice had shaken her head. "I'm sorry," she'd told them. "I'm just not ready." She hadn't added that she wasn't sure she'd ever be. Good, bad, rain-soaked, sunburned, carrying sleepy girls or listening to teenage gripes; every single memory she had of the cottage featured Grahame. Holidays there without him would simply be a reminder of his absence.

Even now, as she fished the enormous key out of her handbag and rattled it into the lock, she realised it had always been Grahame who'd opened the door each time.

It was tricky; the wood was old, and the door needed a shove to get it open. "Allow me," he'd say, and they'd laugh.

Now, pushing her weight against the door, she realised sharply – as she still did every now and then – that he would never be at her side again.

Inside, the cottage smelled of coal and damp, behind it all a tiny scent of mildew which took her back twenty years to the first ever time they'd set foot in the place. At the time, she'd screwed up her nose, wanted to suggest a B&B, to come back the following year when they'd aired it out and had someone in to paint the walls. But Grahame had convinced her. "It's an adventure," he'd said, flinging open the shutters and letting sunlight pour into the neglected rooms. "See, it's already better once you let some light in."

He'd been right – despite the dust and the damp, the creaking taps and draughty bathroom, despite the ramshackle kitchen and temperamental stove, it had been paradise. That's what Grahame had been for her: a different perspective on the world. Rose-tinted. She still tried to see the world as he had – focusing on the positives, however difficult it was to find

ancient TV. In the darkened room, it was difficult to find the catch on the window, but when her hand touched the metal, she lifted it and pulled open the wooden frames. Then, just as Tilly had done in the kitchen and Grahame had done all those years ago, she shoved hard at the wooden shutters, locked together for three years, and sent them flying open.

The air outside the window was fresh, and the room became light and airy once more. She pinned the shutters back on their iron fastenings and, leaving the window ajar, moved to the stairs, making her way carefully up the slightly uneven mahogany and clicking on the light when she reached the landing. From there, it was a few minutes' work to enter each of the three bedrooms to air them out.

Grahame had always been a different perspective for her – a rose tinted one

them. But it was harder these days.

"Come on mum," said Lorna. "I'll get the kettle on."

As Alice sank into a chair, Tilly began opening the stiff wooden kitchen window, pulling the metal of the catch. Then she leaned into the painted shutters and, with a cracking sound, they shuddered open. Light flooded into the small space, highlighting dancing dust particles, and revealing that everywhere was covered with a layer of dirt from the years of neglect. On the table was a magazine, left from their last trip, dated 2019 and curled at the corners. A car magazine. Grahame's magazine.

She mustn't cry in front of the girls.

She stood abruptly. "That will be lovely, Lorna," she said. "I'll just go and…" she allowed the words to trail into silence as she walked into the small living room with its mismatched sofas and

Two of the rooms hadn't been used for years and it would be nice to have the girls sleeping in them once more. *See Grahame*, she wanted to say, *I'm still trying to see the positives.*

The third room was the hardest. Front facing, with its shutters open once more, it yielded a view of the countryside as it tumbled away: fields dotted with trees, thick bushes and woods, and between them a glimpse of the sea beyond. The view she and Grahame had seen each day as they'd sat up in bed to drink their morning tea. Where they'd planned the day's activities and sympathised at each other's sunburn. Where the girls had joined them for cuddles, bouncing their way into the room and onto the bed, full of energy and excitement.

In the light, the room looked exactly the same as they'd left it.

She felt a sob surge through ➡

her body, and leaned her arms down on the bed. Silently, she allowed herself a few tears. Then she wiped her eyes roughly, splashed some water on her face in the en-suite, and made her way back down to the sound of a whistling kettle.

Already, downstairs looked different. Tilly had wiped the table and set out a plate of shortbread. The sunlight had taken the edge from the cold, and the air was fresher. The magazine had been squirrelled away. Both girls looked up at her as she stepped down the last of the stairs and smiled, in the nervous way that people do when they're not sure whether you're OK. She'd seen those looks a lot over the past few years, the tilted eyebrows, furrowed brows.

You hear of people, widowed people like her, moving on. And in the first few months, when she'd felt shrouded in darkness and completely bereft, she'd clung to the notion that grief fades. But it hadn't, not really. You grow around grief someone had told her. You form new connections, new ways of being. You find life despite the ache inside. The loss doesn't shrink, but you grow in spite of it. And she had grown – she'd begun to pick up her life, to move forward. She'd become stronger, able to cope. Yet every

morning. But there was a whole other Grahame – the Grahame from the cottage – and she'd yet to acknowledge his loss.

She'd kept the cottage closed, as if it was a sort of time-capsule. And while she'd reached a place where she could cope with the swell of regret that she felt every time she remembered the cruel motorway pile up that had taken his life – even now, when she remembered his

It's hard because this place is full of memories... but they're good memories

time the girls had suggested going to the cottage, she'd found something inside her stiffen. "No," she'd said, "Not yet."

She'd felt her grief would become raw again if she came to their holiday home. As if she'd mourned for the "home" Grahame – husband, accountant, the man who left damp towels on the bed, but never forgot to bring her a cup of tea each

cheery goodbye as he exited on that last day, she wanted to somehow go back and stop him – she'd become scared of the sharper, newer sense of grief she'd felt sure awaited her in Cornwall.

In reality, by building up this fear of the cottage, she'd denied herself the joy of revisiting places they'd loved, of remembering the fun they'd had together,

both as a family and as a couple – of feeling the sharp sting of missing him, yes, but growing around that too. In the way Grahame would have encouraged her to do had he been here.

She'd been scared to let the light in.

"Wow, you two are well trained," she quipped, as Lorna began to pour water into the china teapot and Tilly pulled out one of the wooden chairs for her to sit in.

Tilly laughed. "Well, we had a good teacher," she said. "It was always tea and biscuits the second we arrived."

"You used to turn your noses up!" said Alice, as she sank gratefully into the chair. What was it about being a passenger that made you so tired?

"Ah, but we loved it really," said Lorna, placing the pot on the table and setting out three mugs. "We were just far too cool to acknowledge it."

Tilly bit into a shortbread. A sprinkle of crumbs scattered onto the wooden table. She brushed them onto the floor and Alice had to suppress a laugh. Not everything had changed.

"Shall we take a walk up to St Genny's?" suggested Lorna. "Just a couple of miles, and we can stop at the café afterwards?"

"Sounds perfect," Alice said.

The girls glanced at each other. Then Tilly said it, "So is it weird… you know… being back?" she reached out her hand and touched Alice's shoulder. "I mean, because you thought… you know. You were worried…" her eyes searched her mother's face.

"A bit," said Alice. "Me and your dad… well, there's a lot of memories."

Tilly nodded and Lorna shifted her chair closer to Alice's.

"But they're good memories," Alice added. "I mean, it's hard, isn't it? It's hard for all of us without your dad. But coming here… it's reminded me of how good your dad was at, well, making it fun. Seeing things positively, even on the days when things went wrong." ➤

Lorna smiled.

"Yes, like that time when I got my trainers totally drenched."

"Or the time that wave knocked the camera out of his hand."

"And do you remember that seagull that snatched Mum's ice-cream? He said it was good luck or something!"

"And when I got stung on my foot, and he carried me down the cliff path."

"Oh yes! I remember that!"

"And he said not to worry that he'd needed the exercise."

"Do you remember the sandcastle competition?"

realise that he is here, sort of."

"In our memories?" Lorna suggested.

"Well, yes. In those, of course. And actually it's lovely to remember the things that happened here – things I'd forgotten. Good times. But I suppose I meant that he's here, isn't he, in us," Alice said.

"What, me and Tilly?"

"Well, yes, but kind of in me too. Your father, he taught me how to see the world differently. To see a setback and find the positive in it. To… to throw open the blinds first thing in the morning to…"

"… let the light in," said Tilly, with a

A wave of sadness came over them all, like a wave breaking on the beach

"And remember that time when he tried to teach mum to skim stones?"

"When he met that man who said he could tell fortunes?"

"When we hired that rowing boat and almost ended up getting capsized?"

They were all laughing now, finding it hard to get the words out.

Then the moment passed, the laughing stopped as a wash of sadness came over them all, like a wave breaking on a beach.

Tilly said. "I wish he was here."

"Tilly!" Lorna admonished, casting a sideways glance at Alice.

"Well, I do. I miss him. It's OK to say it, isn't it?" Tilly replied.

"Yes," Alice said. "Of course it is. And of course you do. We all do."

The silence descended again. Alice took a sip of her tea.

"But," she added. "But I'm starting to

grin. "He was always saying that."

"Yes: *what are you doing sitting in the dark?*" Lorna mimicked.

"He was right though, wasn't he?" Alice reached for her daughters' hands and squeezed them. "I've been sitting in the dark for too long. It's time to start living again."

And as the sunlight streamed through the newly-opened windows, as the girls pulled a map from a drawer and began to plan their route, Alice finally felt herself step out of the shadows. Ⓜ️

MY INSPIRATION

I'm inspired by everyday life: a beautiful view, an unexplored place, by people – their eccentricities, flaws, courage or kindness – and the "ordinary miracles" that happen every day.

Brain Boosters

Sudoku 1   Sudoku 2

Fill in each of the blank squares with the numbers 1 to 9, so that each row, each column and each 3x3 cell contains all the numbers from 1 to 9.

Sudoku 1

		9						
	6			5				3
		3		1				6
3			8	2		1		
	5			6				7
9			1	3		4		
		5		8				1
	4			7				8
		1						

Sudoku 2

		2					4	
1					3	2	6	
	5			6		9		
		9	1				2	
			9					
		8	4				1	
	3			1		6		
6					2	4	8	
		1					3	

Word Wheel

Turn To Page 157 For Solutions

You have ten minutes to find as many words as possible using the letters in the wheel. Each word must be three letters or more and contain the central letter. Use each letter once and no plurals, foreign words or porper nouns are allowed. There is at least one nine-letter word.

Average: 33 words
Good: 34-50 words
Excellent: 51-66 words

House Proud

Home is where the heart is, but Lucy's heart had been lost and homeless for so many years…

By Marie Penman

Despite the saying "There's no place like home", and the general belief that home was where the heart was, Lucy found that the further she drove from her beige bungalow in the suburbs, the happier she felt. She had a whole week off work and was delighted to be heading north, into the countryside, to spend a few days with her beloved aunt.

Maisie was in her late seventies now but was still sharp as a tack and as fit as many fifty-somethings that Lucy knew. She suspected this was down to the fact that Maisie had never married or had children, but had opted instead for a long and productive career in the civil service. As a child, Lucy had gazed at this formidable woman with awe and respect, but as she grew older, the two had become close friends and allies.

Maisie was what many would describe as a "character", meaning she was confident, forthright and outspoken. As the younger sister of Lucy's dad, she would probably have been expected to marry young, raise a family and run an efficient household, none of which she had done. Instead, she had worked in London, made a very comfortable living, and then ➡

finally returned home to Orchard House, the home in the country that the family had lived in for generations, to care for her elderly parents.

Lucy had nothing but fond memories of Orchard House, having spent all her summers there as a child. Arriving there from the city, it had felt like paradise, with its lush green lawn, its fruit trees (perfect for climbing!) and its slower pace of life that had offered such an escape.

And escape was what Lucy was looking and hoping for again. After a terrible few months, during which time her marriage to Pete had finally imploded, her only son Jacob had moved out to live with his girlfriend, and the cat had died, Lucy just wanted to get away. It had been a long, hard winter – in more ways than one – and with spring finally showing signs of appearing, this trip to Orchard House meant everything to Lucy.

The clocks had gone forward the previous weekend – at last! – so there was unloading her bags, the front door was flung open and Maisie appeared with a huge grin on her face.

"Lucy, you're here!" she called out. "It's been too long!"

And in truth, it had been quite a while since the two women had spent any time together. Lucy and Pete had finally split up at the end of January, staggering through one final Christmas together, and since then, Lucy had been packing up boxes, emptying wardrobes, and generally removing all evidence of her errant husband from her life.

"Is he finally gone then?" Maisie asked. "All boxes removed?"

Lucy nodded, smiled at her aunt's customary bluntness, then promptly burst into tears as she fell into her arms.

An hour later, sitting in front of the log fire with a mug of tea, a chunk of gingerbread cake and her aunt sitting opposite her, Lucy told her tale of woe.

"I don't even know why I'm crying,

Lucy felt so grateful to be back in Orchard House, where it felt like home

still light in the sky when Lucy turned her car into the driveway at Orchard House two hours later. As always, just the sight of the old place lifted her spirits.

The honey-coloured stone of the house glowed golden in the early evening sunshine and the front garden was showing signs of waking up from winter, with clusters of daffodils, snowdrops and crocuses scattered around. There were half a dozen rhododendron bushes in front of the windows that Lucy knew would soon burst into colour, and the twisted cherry tree by the front door seemed to wrap its branches around the home, keeping it safe and secure.

As Lucy got out of her car and started

Maisie – Lord knows I was glad to see the back of Pete – but it's just been such a stressful couple of months, what with him leaving, then Jacob packing up, then Misty the cat…" Lucy's voice faded away as the tears returned.

Maisie gave her a firm hug and another piece of cake.

"Poor Lucy – you've had a hellish time of it," she said. "But you're here now and in a few days, you'll be back to full strength. As for Pete, well, good riddance is all I can say – you were always too good for him!"

And Lucy laughed and cried and felt so happy and grateful to be back in Orchard House, really the only place that had truly felt like home in her life.

Lucy had only been eleven when her mum had died, leaving her poor dad to bring her up alone. They'd both relied heavily on the grandparents – and Maisie, too – and without those long summers spent entirely at Orchard House, Lucy wasn't sure she would have survived her childhood.

With Maisie's encouragement, however, she had stuck in at school, passed her exams and gone off to university to study English literature, where her creative side had been allowed to flourish and she'd immersed herself in books and poetry.

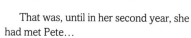

That was, until in her second year, she had met Pete…

He was a bit older than her, working as a bar manager, and had seemed fun and exciting to Lucy, who was getting fed up with earnest, serious young student boyfriends. Within a couple of months, they were practically living together – and not long after that, Lucy had discovered she was pregnant.

Without a mum to advise her, and too embarrassed to tell her dad or grandparents, Lucy had turned to Maisie for help, who said she'd support Lucy whatever her decision.

Then Pete had turned up at her student flat and suggested they get married, which had seemed hopelessly romantic to twenty-year-old Lucy. Despite Maisie's pleas to reconsider, she had dropped out of university to become a wife and raise a baby.

Now, she felt nothing but foolish and embarrassed.

Although it had all ended badly, she still had Jacob, of course, her darling son who was now twenty-three, living with his girlfriend and working as a joiner. So however awful Lucy's relationship with Pete had been – and at times, it had been horrendous – something wonderful had come of it in the form of her lovely Jacob.

That night over dinner, Lucy and Maisie talked over old times and discussed the future.

"Are you going to sell the house?" Maisie asked. "Getting rid of it could be the one good thing to come out of your divorce…"

It was true that Lucy did not really care for her marital home. The beige bungalow had never suited her – she considered herself far more colourful than that. It was Pete and his mum who had picked it out when they'd been looking to buy all those years ago, which made it all the more ironic that it was Lucy who had ended up living there alone.

Lucy nodded as she crammed more pasta into her mouth. "Yeah, I guess, though I'm going to have to find somewhere else first – a flat, I suppose – and take a serious look at my finances…" ➤

She shuddered. "It's a grim situation – I'm not really sure what I'm going to do next."

"Take your time," Maisie said. "You still have your whole life in front of you… Why don't you think about going back to university and finishing your degree?"

Lucy laughed. "A student again, at my age? I love your optimism, Maisie, but I think that stage of my life has passed."

"Nonsense!" Maisie said briskly. "Think of this as a new chapter, Lucy – it's up to you to write your next adventure…"

Which made Lucy cry again, at the kindness and support from this woman who had never wavered in all the years they had known each other.

They continued chatting until late into the night, before Maisie suggested that they spend a bit of time over the next few days doing some spring cleaning.

Lucy was surprised. "Wow, that's unlike you, Maisie. No offence, but you've never been especially houseproud…"

Maisie shrugged. "True, but the old house is looking a bit tired – I haven't done anything to it since your granny died four years ago." She smiled at her niece. "You're so much better at fixing and organising things than me – it can be a team effort."

So the next day, the women washed, scrubbed and polished, throwing out piles of old newspapers, broken gadgets and anything else that was judged surplus to requirements.

Although the kitchen looked a lot cleaner and more spacious afterwards, there was no denying it was still pretty old and faded. Lucy looked around as the two women sat having a coffee at the big table.

"I tell you what, Maisie," said Lucy. "I could sand down the cupboard doors and repaint them in a nice bright colour – they'd look brand new."

"Can you be bothered?" Maisie asked. "That sounds like a lot of work…"

Lucy shrugged. "What else have I got to do? And to be honest, I'd welcome the distraction from the misery of my own life."

Lucy had always loved interior design and DIY, and obsessively watched home improvement programmes on TV. Unfortunately, the bungalow was less than inspiring, with its plain walls and absence of character, so any grand designs she'd had remained locked in her head. Now, at Orchard House, Maisie told her to do pretty much whatever she wanted.

Lucy spent hours sanding and painting the kitchen units, which looked so much better in a sunshine yellow paint, then she phoned Jacob and asked if he had any free time. Next day, her son arrived and fitted new beech worktops in the kitchen, as well as repairing the old window frames and faded shutters on the outside of the house.

"I'd forgotten how great this place was, Auntie M," he remarked, as he sat drinking tea at the end of the day. "I'll come back at the weekend and do a few more bits and pieces – maybe build some shelves into the alcoves in the living room so you can get all your books stored properly."

Maisie hugged him. "Jacob, you're a gem! Definitely my favourite great-nephew!"

He laughed. "And your only one!"

Jacob recommended a friend who was a plumber, and Lucy called him to get a price for fitting a new bathroom.

Maisie decided it was long overdue and told Lucy to choose whatever style she wanted, and maybe get a price for a new boiler at the same time.

Which meant that despite having to go home at the end of her week's break, Lucy came back to Orchard House pretty much every weekend after that to oversee the home improvements.

The work was giving some much needed purpose to her life, which, apart from her dull job in the admin department of a leisure centre, offered very little in the way of excitement.

flooring, but so many scenes from the past – her childhood games, her dear old grandparents, and her dad, who had died when Jacob was just a toddler.

In truth, if he'd still been around, Lucy doubted she'd have stayed with Pete as long as she did, but without her parents – officially an orphan – she'd felt hopeless and lost, clinging to Pete and her small family for support. And to give her ex-husband his due, he'd been nothing but kind to her as she'd drowned in her grief for months.

But what now? Her family seemed to be shrinking again, as Jacob moved on in his life with Chloe, and Pete reinvented himself as a single man – Lucy had already spotted his page on Tinder.

It felt like a chapter in Lucy's life was closing, yet she felt unsure about what was meant to happen next. All she could do was continue cleaning and painting the old house, seeing it slowly come to life again, as if she was colouring in a faded picture in a story book.

A chapter in Lucy's life was closing and she felt unsure what to do next

As the days got lighter and the weather improved, her trips back to Maisie's place to continue the spring cleaning and decorating felt less like a chore and more like a treat. Her aunt still had an active social life, meeting friends for walks or lunches in the nearby town, meaning Lucy was often alone in the big house, silently painting skirting boards or varnishing doors.

It really was a beautiful home, full of comfort and warmth, which made the return to her own place at the end of the weekends harder and harder.

She often paused in her work to look around the old house, seeing not just the thick stone walls and the oak

The work was all finished by the start of May, just in time for a mini heatwave, meaning Lucy could turn her attentions to the garden, a bit overgrown but still the lush paradise of her childhood memories.

Maisie occasionally took a trowel and tinkered around the edges, pulling up the odd weed, while Lucy mowed the lawn and cut back the trees.

"Let's have a house-warming party, Lucy!" Maisie suddenly announced one weekend. "For your birthday in a couple of weeks. What do you say?"

Lucy paused for a moment and wiped the sweat from her face.

"Well, it probably won't surprise you ➡

to learn that I have no plans for my birthday, so sure, a party would be lovely!" She frowned. "Who could we invite?"

Maisie laughed. "I'll put the word out in my social circle and let the neighbours know as well. You get Jacob and Chloe here, and invite anyone else you want."

So a party it was, with fairy lights strung through the trees, candles on all the window sills and new garden furniture set out under a gazebo that Jacob and Chloe had erected for the occasion.

"What's this?" She quickly read it.

"Maisie, I don't understand…"

"It's the deeds to the house – your house." Maisie explained that she'd transferred the ownership of Orchard House to Lucy, and she was moving into a new flat she'd bought in town, close to her friends and the shops.

"I'm a city girl at heart," Maisie said. "All those years in London – I need to be near the hustle and bustle. But you… well,

"Happy birthday," Maisie said, giving her an envelope. "You deserve this"

Lucy had never seen the house look so beautiful. The windows gleamed, the stonework sparkled and the flowers and bushes in the garden were a riot of colour. Maisie brought her a glass of champagne before the other guests arrived and toasted her niece with a smile.

"You've transformed the place, Lucy – I'm proud of you."

Lucy smiled. "I think the house has transformed me, to be honest – it got me through a tough time and made me feel like me again…"

Maisie hugged her, then handed her a thick cream coloured envelope.

"Happy birthday, sweetheart. You deserve this."

Lucy took the envelope and grinned, expecting it to be a gift voucher for the local garden centre or something similar.

She opened it to find a printed document on official headed notepaper and frowned as she looked at her aunt.

you've always loved it here, Lucy. And anyway, you were due to inherit the house after I died, but to be honest, I'd rather give it to you now."

Lucy felt her eyes fill with tears again as she laughed and sobbed at the same time.

"Seriously, Maisie – is this for real?"

Maisie laughed. "Of course! This house was made for you, Lucy. And I think you've had quite enough sadness in your life – it's time for your happy ever after."

As Lucy wiped away her tears, and laughed aloud in sheer joy, she suddenly understood that this home was definitely where her heart was… **MW**

MY INSPIRATION

I think it has to be love that inspires me. I'm married to the man of my dreams – seriously! – and we have four amazing children together. Every day of my life, I think about how lucky I am.

48
Calories per
tbsp

Luxury Mincemeat

Ingredients (Makes about 1.6kg)

- ◆ **200g sultanas**
- ◆ **200g currants**
- ◆ **200g raisins**
- ◆ **100g dried cranberries**
- ◆ **100g mixed peel**
- ◆ **2tsp mixed spice**
- ◆ **½tsp freshly grated nutmeg**
- ◆ **250g light brown muscovado sugar**
- ◆ **150g butter, cut into small pieces**
- ◆ **50g whole blanched almonds, cut into slivers**
- ◆ **grated zest and juice 1 lemon**
- ◆ **225g Bramley cooking apple, peeled, cored and finely chopped**
- ◆ **150ml brandy or sherry**

1 Combine everything except the brandy or sherry in a saucepan and mix. Heat gently, stirring until the butter melts. Gently cook for 5 minutes, stirring 3-4 times. Leave to cool.

2 Stir in the alcohol. Spoon into sterilised jars. Cover with waxed discs and seal. Allow to mature for 2 weeks.   ➜ **127**

Dancing In The Moonlight

How was bookish Cynthia to catch the attention of the only man who had sparked her interest?

By H. Johnson-Mack

Cynthia Maitland gazed dispassionately at her reflection. Not much for her poor step-mama to work with, though Amelie was doing her best to find someone for Cynthia to marry.

Spending her life with a father who'd indulged her thirst for knowledge was something Cynthia didn't want to relinquish. If only she could find a man who would embrace that side of her. But not everyone shared Papa's liberal mind.

A masked ball, inviting eligible bachelors and one gentleman in particular, had seemed a good idea. Now she wasn't sure.

A tap on the door and Lady Amelie entered her bedchamber. The former widow had a flower-like fragility that tonight was enhanced by a gentian-blue gown. No wonder Papa had been smitten!

"How lovely you look, Mama," said Cynthia, laughing emphasis placed on Amelie's new title. "'Tis fortunate for us younger ladies you're to be masked or we wouldn't get a single dance!"

Amelie disclaimed, blushing, and lifting Cynthia's half-mask, fixed it into position.

"I wish you'd reconsider," she murmured. "I understand your reticence where finding a husband is concerned, but is this test the right way to go about things?"

Cynthia cupped Amelie's cheek.

"Whatever is meant to be, will be."

I'll get even with you for this, Olivia, Ashley Beaumont vowed as he threaded his way through the masked guests. His sister was determined that as heir to the family estates, he should do his duty and marry well. Ashley was content to let her enjoy wedded bliss (or in her case, comfortable convenience) and take his time finding a meeting of minds.

His sister Alice was to blame for this romanticism; she'd married for love, and he was never as happy as when he was with Alice's family. Was it so wrong to want that for himself?

It was partly out of guilt of this favouritism, partly to prove Olivia wrong for once, he'd agreed to attend this ball at Maitlands, home of Olivia's old friend, new husband and stepdaughter. He hated these affairs. They were so phoney, and he knew hardly anybody here. Impeccable manners and smoothness on the dance floor never compensated for the shyness he suffered in unfamiliar company.

At least he was masked, he reflected as he arrived before his hosts. It eased things.

He bent over the hand of Olivia's friend, now Lady Maitland, smothering a groan at sight of the maid by her side.

So this was why Olivia insisted he attended! Cynthia Maitland, obviously on display as a potential bride, appeared colourless and no doubt clueless as she murmured a hope that he enjoy the evening.

They moved together. In the ghostly world the moon made phantoms of them both

He watched her join the dance set just forming. Well, she had grace. But if Olivia thought this was the woman he'd been waiting for, she really didn't know him at all.

The ball was well underway, guests enjoying Amelie's hired musicians, when Cynthia decided it was time she took a hand in her own affairs. How nervous she felt, now the moment was upon her. It didn't help that the room was so stuffy and her gown so tight across her chest.

She approached the alcove where Ashley Beaumont stood alone. She'd seen him in London; a tall, personable gentleman whom she believed shared her secret passion. Now, when she could finally talk to him, she was tongue-tied. Too late to retreat; he had asked if she liked the ball.

"Yes, to my surprise."

"Surprise?"

"Don't you ever tire of wearing masks, pretending to be something you're not?"

His brows rose.

"Why, yes, as a matter of fact –"

Whatever he'd been about to add was lost with the arrival of a fashionable English Rose in ivory satin and peacock mask.

"Excuse me," he said, gaze focused on the newcomer as he moved away. ➤

Cynthia's heart sank. Amelie was right. Men seldom acted as you wished. Pretty faces were all they seemed to value.

"Good evening, Sophy. Is that another new gown?"

The young lady laughed.

"Why, Beau, you actually look pleased to see me!"

"I am. I know hardly anyone here."

"Poor boy. What about the sparrow you were with just now?"

Recalling the potentially interesting conversation Sophy had interrupted, Ashley turned to where he'd been standing with Miss Maitland. But the alcove was empty.

Cynthia waited until dark before she slipped into the gardens. She was right – no cloud to obscure the heavens. She'd be able to drink them in to her heart's content.

It was cold but blissfully quiet, a whisper of breeze stirring sleeping shrubs and skeletal trees. Perfect for thinking, dreaming… but what was she dreaming about? Not the ball; that had proved to be another lame horse on life's racetrack. She'd hoped that this time, things might be different. It seemed it wasn't to be.

Her gaze strayed upward out of habit, and stayed on a sigh. Mama had taught her there were different kinds of love. Romance was magical, and something surely all hearts craved, if only a little. She smiled as something in the night sky seemed to wink at her. Ah, well. If her destiny was only to find love in knowledge and study, what an adventure that would be…

After dancing with Sophy and her friend, Ashley felt able to take his leave. It was a beautifully clear night, the moon casting her pearly glow over Maitlands' gardens. It wasn't that far to his lodgings so on a whim, he struck out toward the parkland. He'd always loved walking in the moonlight. And it seemed he wasn't the only one…

"You may as well come out," he told the figure who'd been twirling round the garden then darted behind a tree at his arrival. "The moon gave you away."

Cynthia Maitland, sans mask, appeared in the shaft of light that had revealed her.

"I took you for a fairy sprite," he began, smiling as she murmured, "Perhaps I am."

"Why did you leave the party, little fairy? You do not care for balls?"

"Not when compared with all this." She looked round the silver-tipped grounds then up to the heavens. "Everything feels so different in the moonlight, do you not think? And the stars… as old as time itself, and as endlessly fascinating."

Was he dreaming? Ashley wondered. Was this woman confessing to a love of something he'd followed all his life?

"Fascinating, indeed," he murmured. "You like the stars, then?"

"What is it you would prefer to hear?" she asked a little sharply. "That they're pretty but not as nice as gowns and ribbons? If I say that, will you stay talking to me?"

Ashley blinked then shook his head.

"What is this world I've stumbled into?"

"A better one than that in there, perhaps," she murmured then suddenly laughed. "Oh, I'm sorry, sir. The moon and stars are making me mad, and you uncomfortable. Please, go back to the ball, or wherever you were headed."

"I'd rather stay and dance with you."

The strings of the musicians could just be heard upon the breeze as they struck up a new tune. The hand that held her mask began to tremble. Ashley held out his own.

"May I have this dance, little fairy?"

She hesitated then stepped closer, allowing him to guide her into the dance. They moved together, then apart, sidestepping, hands touching then withdrawing, in a ghostly world where the moon made phantoms of them both. Finally, the music stopped, and they ceased to move, fingertips raised to each other's.

Ashley drew in a breath.

"Are you real?" he muttered.

She stepped back with a shaky laugh.

"None of this is real," she whispered. "The moon can make us believe in nonsense. I must flee her dangerous influence, and you should, too, sir." She began to back away, then added, "And save yourself any more awkward balls by doing only what you choose from now on."

She flitted away into the shadows.

Ashley stared after her, his smile wry.

Dash it, Olivia, he cursed inwardly at last. *It appears you're right again…*

Cynthia was fiddling with her hair next morning when Amelie flew into the bedroom, a card in fluttering fingers.

"Oh, Cyn, love, Ashley Beaumont has written, asking to take you out today!"

Cynthia blinked.

"Would you allow me to see him alone, please, darling? I believe there's been some mistake, but I'll soon straighten it out."

A winter sun was spilling golden light through Maitlands' drawing-room windows onto Turkish rugs and the profile of Miss Cynthia. When Ashley entered, she turned and regarded him solemnly. Her eyes were a soft, clear grey, her dress sprig muslin embroidered with silver stars.

"I've come to invite you to the Royal Observatory, Miss Maitland," he began. "There's a lecture on astronomy I believe you'd find as fascinating as I do."

"Me?" she asked. When he nodded, she frowned. "What then?"

"I'd take you driving, perhaps, or on a picnic. All the things you do when you're getting to know someone better."

"And you want to know me better, sir?" Ashley laughed.

"Is that so hard to believe?"

"Mr Beaumont, I've something to confess. I saw you talk at an astronomy lecture in London last season and found myself thinking of you. So I bullied my poor step-mama into inviting you to our ball.

"My plan was to entice you into the garden, show you the stars. But I realise now what impression my flitting round the garden alone might have given you." She sighed. "I also learned your heart desires fashionable English rose, not dull brown."

Ashley's emphatic denial made her start.

"But that beautiful blonde last night…"

"Sophy's lovely, yes. She's also my cousin and a royal pain most of the time. I was happy to see her; she was the only person I knew. But I want companionship, intelligence and someone happy to avoid society events. In short I believe I want you."

"And I believe you're still suffering from a touch of moongazy!"

"Perhaps. I'd like to take the advice of my fairy sprite, and from now on do only what I choose."

"Which is?" Cynthia drew in a breath.

He came to sit beside her, lifting her chin so he could look into her eyes.

"To see whether I'm right in my belief that last night, I discovered the woman I've been searching the stars for, someone I could share my interests with as well as my life. So do you think you could come to Greenwich with me, help me find out?"

Her smile was all he'd hoped.

"I do…" **MW**

MY INSPIRATION

There's something very magical about moonlight, and dancing – in whatever century you happen to live – is even more romantic when it's performed under the silvery light of the moon!

Good Neighbours!

Angie wished she could do something about the nuisances next door – and then fell upon the solution!

By Kate Hogan

Y ou'll have to do something about your rats, Angie," Margie shouted. I stared across the garden, wishing I could do something about my crazy neighbour, before slinking inside the little house I'd been so pleased to buy until I met Margie!

"I hope you're planning on cutting down that tree at the front," she'd shouted the day I'd moved in.

"But it's a lovely ornamental cherry," I said. "Beautiful in flower, its petals are…"

"All over my front," she answered.

I felt a sick, sinking feeling inside. I hadn't thought I'd need to vet the neighbours for niceness before signing up for the mortgage. Compromise, I told myself, with a deep sigh. Don't start on the wrong foot. Just trim the tree a little.

Every time our paths crossed, Margie had a litany of complaints.

So I'd trimmed the tree, and kept the sound of my music and TV so low they were barely audible. I even parked my car down the street, because apparently it would make it impossible for emergency services to access Margie's property if my car was parked on the road directly outside my own house!

But now rats! I'd not seen a single rat. I hardly ever saw a single other neighbour, either – out at work most days, probably, like me. No children or teenagers kicking up a rumpus. In fact it was so quiet, I couldn't imagine why Margie was always on the warpath.

But rats… that was a bridge too far.

I would put the house back on the market, look for somewhere with better neighbours. I decided I'd start scrolling through the local estate agents right away.

H ours later I was almost asleep with the boredom of it all, finding nothing as quaint and interesting as the house I was living in, and thinking how miserable the whole situation was, when I heard the scratching sound. Rats! Wanting to run and hide, I knew I'd have to investigate.

Peering through the kitchen window with one ear cocked, I guessed maybe it was just a branch from the Wisteria tapping on the window. It was another thing I loved about the house, all the old cottage garden type bushes and plants.

Pulling open the kitchen door to ➡

Every time our paths crossed, Margie had a litany of complaints

see if I was right, I'd hardly stepped outside when a flash of something at the back of the garden caught my eye.

"A cat!" I said as it darted into the old brick shed.

The little mewling family of two kittens, hidden in a recess and shielded by the mother cat tore at my heart. I'd always wanted a cat, but how could I when I worked all day?

"Poor little things, I'll get you some food," I whispered excitedly, before spinning back to the door. The scream,

vulnerable she looked. "It was just that I heard scratching, while I was scrolling through the estate agents, sites," I added, gingerly standing with Margie's support, "I thought that maybe…"

"You're not thinking of leaving, I hope. Nice neighbour like you…"

"I…" I began, lost for words.

"How's the ankle feeling?" she asked, once I was settled on the couch, frozen peas out of her freezer wrapped round my ankle. "Maybe we could keep the little

My foot caught in the washing line and my scream alerted the whole town!

as my foot caught in the tangled washing line, was enough to alert the whole town!

I lay there stunned, pain clamping my ankle, just as all the outside lights next door went on. Margie came through the side gate wild eyed with anger, but suddenly the look of fury faded.

"You're hurt!" she said, rushing to check my condition. "Poor girl," she added, an unexpected look of tenderness on her face. "What happened?"

"Cats, not rats… in the shed – little family of them, two kittens and…"

"Kittens!" said Margie, her face lighting up. "We'll have to look after them. But we'll have to look after you first. I used to be a nurse you know. Let's see if you can put any weight on the ankle. You shouldn't have been out here in the dark anyway – checking for rats… it's all my silly, fault going on about something and nothing all the time. I'm so sorry."

"That's OK," I said, seeing how

furry family. I'd be able to keep an eye out for your kitten while you're at work. I could keep the mum cat, too."

"You could – you would?" I said thinking of my long awaited wish of a fluffy little friend coming true.

"For now, though, your ankle is more important – how's it feeling?"

"Quite painful," I fibbed, wincing, even though it wasn't hurting at all anymore. "It's very kind of you to help me like this, Margie… very neighbourly."

"What neighbours are for. I'm sure you'd do the same for me…"

"Of course I would," I said, touching her hand. Suddenly knowing I would. Ⓜ

MY INSPIRATION

I'm a good listener and am continually inspired by the stories people tell me, which show how many difficulties can be overcome with love and friendship.

171
Calories per serving

Panforte

Ingredients
(Makes 24 slices)

- **125g blanched hazelnuts**
- **125g blanched whole almonds**
- **200g candied mixed peel**
- **50g ground almonds**
- **125g plain flour**
- **100g dried apricots, chopped**
- **1tsp ground cinnamon**
- **½tsp ground coriander**
- **½tsp freshly grated nutmeg**
- **150g runny honey**
- **150g caster sugar**
- **icing sugar, to dust**

1 Grease and line a 20cm spring-form cake tin with non-stick baking paper. Preheat the oven to 180°C/ Fan 160°C/Gas 4. Place the hazelnuts and almonds on a baking tray and bake for 7-10min, until light golden. Cool and chop coarsely.

2 Lower the oven to 150°C/ Fan 140°C/Gas 2. Put the chopped nuts, candied peel, ground almonds, flour, chopped apricots and spices in a bowl and mix together. Put the honey and sugar in a saucepan and heat gently, stirring occasionally until it is dissolved.

3 Bring to the boil and heat gently for 3-4min or until it reaches 115°C. Remove from the heat. Working very quickly, stir in the nut mixture and transfer to the prepared tin. Bake for 40-45min until still soft, but not sticky. Place the tin on a wire rack where the panforte will harden as it cools.

4 Turn out and remove the baking paper. Dredge the top with icing sugar. Store in an airtight container for up to a month. Serve cut into thin slices. ➜ **133**

The Sherbet Dab Ride

London cab drivers might well look out for each other, but would she be charmed by her latest passenger?

By Julia Douglas

The schools are out and Wandsworth Road is packed with four-wheel drives more suited to an arctic expedition. Nobody thinks to let a lady taxi driver out of a side street until another cabbie flashes his lights.

I've barely joined the traffic when a woman in a red coat thrusts her arm in the air and yells, "Taxi!"

I raise a palm in apology and jerk my thumb at the cab behind. The other taxi driver gives me a thumbs up as he pulls in to pick her up. She would have been his fare if he hadn't let me out, after all. We cabbies watch out for each other, you see.

A hundred yards down the road, my good deed is rewarded. I'm hailed by a sticks a grinning, square jawed and incredibly handsome face through the open passenger window and I realise he definitely hasn't been in my cab before.

"Anywhere in particular?" I ask as I pull my phone from its dashboard holder.

"Do you know the White Duck restaurant?" he says as he climbs in the back. "I'm meeting some friends there."

"No problem. Sorry, I thought I had a text." I drop the phone back into its holder and start the meter.

Spotting a gap in the oncoming traffic, I pull a sharp U-turn and make the tyres squeal as I goose the accelerator.

"Um, shouldn't we be going that way?" My handsome passenger nervously points over his shoulder.

"Only if you want to be stuck in the

I'm hailed by an incredibly handsome young man in an expensive looking coat

young man in a smart suit and expensive-looking dogtooth coat.

His blond curls look strangely familiar, although that's not unusual.

When you pick up 25 people day in a city like London it can be hard to tell whether you've driven someone before or saw them on *EastEnders* the previous evening.

"Islington High Street, please." He road works at Vauxhall Bridge." My earrings swing in the sunshine as I signal right and turn into an empty street. "This way will save you a good fifteen minutes."

"Ah, the famous Knowledge, eh?" Mr Handsome grins in my rear-view mirror as he settles back in the centre of the black leather upholstery.

"That's what you pay for when you hail a black cab," I wink. ➤

As a teenager, I threaded my way through these back streets and 25,000 others on a scooter with a map stand on the handlebars, memorising every square, crescent, cul-de-sac and alley in the London A-Z. Sometimes a grizzled old cabbie would pull alongside me at the lights and say, "You're wasting your time, luv. This game's finished." Even twenty years ago there were those who thought it was a dying trade. Lord knows what they'd make of it today, with all the ride-sharing apps undercutting our prices.

I'd loved my dad's cab since I was a child, though. I adored the mirror-like paintwork he seemed to spend every spare moment washing and polishing. I loved the smell of the upholstery and the

Do they still do the Knowledge?" Mr Handsome asks, as we breeze over Chelsea Bridge. "I mean, with SatNav, can't you just punch in the address?"

I chuckle at how often I've heard that remark, even from aspiring cabbies when I've dropped in to give them a pep talk at a Knowledge school.

"SatNav will never beat a London cabbie," I say proudly. "In fact, I proved that on TV last year in a programme called *Cabbie v SatNav* – my one claim to fame."

"I thought I'd seen you somewhere before!" My well-dressed passenger snaps his fingers and leans forward with interest. His woody cologne mixes with the cool air blowing up from the Thames as I turn onto the Embankment.

He walked to his sherbet – from Cockney rhyming slang: sherbert dab, cab

amount of room in the back when he'd whisk the family down to Brighton for a day at the sea. Most of all, I loved the fact that he could take us to the coast whenever the mood and weather suited. As master of his own cab, he could work whenever he pleased. I couldn't wait to get a green badge of my own.

It takes most people between two and four years to pass the Knowledge, although when I say most, I mean a minority, because more than three quarters of those who attempt it drop out. I had my badge a little more than a year after I passed my driving test, thanks to Dad's schooling.

Every dinnertime, Mum would roll her eyes at the end of the table while Dad said, "Take me from the Tate Modern to Scotland Yard."

"Easy," I'd grin, as I summoned up the map in my mind. "Straight up Holland Street, then right into Summer Street…"

"They had me race an actual racing driver from one side of London to the other in the rush hour," I recount. "I was halfway there before he'd typed in the address and I'd finished my coffee at the other end before he finally turned up.

"It's not just about knowing the shortcuts, though," I add, as I swing into another side street. "For instance, if you wanted to know the best restaurant to impress a date and you wanted to stop at a cash point on the way, then a flower stall to pick up a red rose, your SatNav wouldn't be able to help. But with me, it's all up here." I tap my blonde bob.

"What if I wanted to impress *you* with a fancy restaurant," my dishy fare lowers his voice, seductively. "Which one would you pick?"

His hazel eyes twinkle flirtatiously in the mirror and I wonder if he's being serious – he looks a few years younger than me, after all. The boldness of his gaze brings a flush to my cheeks.

"Claridges," I say decisively. "I'd pick the table under the clock and have the lobster thermidor with champagne."

Mr Handsome cracks up.

"Don't laugh!" I protest. "Us cabbies have expensive tastes. That's where my husband took me on our first date."

"Is he a cabbie, too?"

"Yeah, we're the only people who understand why we do this job."

As we pass one of the ornate green Victorian cabmen's shelters that are still dotted around London, I see a leathery white-haired man with mirrored sunglasses walking to his sherbet as we call them – from the Cockney rhyming slang: sherbet dab, cab.

I tap my horn and give him an OK sign. He nods back.

"That's Shades, on account of his sunglasses," I tell my passenger. "We all have nicknames, you see, like Freddie the Fib, who's always telling porkies about how much he's earning or the famous people he's had in the back of his cab."

"What's your nickname?" Mr Handsome eyes me keenly.

"They call me Tommy, because of all the tomfoolery I wear." I tap my dangly earring and finger the gold chain at my throat. I may not do the most glamorous job in the world, but I always try to keep up appearances, even if my passengers only ever see me from the shoulders up.

"Don't you ever feel unsafe as a woman in a cab on your own?" His silk-over-steel tone suddenly puts me on edge. "I mean, you never know who you're going to pick up, do you?"

"Smile, you're on camera." I point to the little CCTV camera trained on the back of the cab. "I've also got a panic button. The police would be here pretty quick if I needed them."

We didn't have any of those safety measures when I started – you had to use your wits. I suppose I was young and fearless. Or maybe young and foolish. But I was never afraid to work nights, because that's where the money was.

Come 10pm you'd always find me down the Strand in time for what we call "the burst", when everyone floods out of the theatres. After that it was pub closing time. Then, in the small hours, we'd wait for the clubs to turn out. The milk floats were on the streets when I finally made my way home.

It was hard slog and I wouldn't like to do it now. These days I keep more sociable hours. But I'm glad I did those night shifts because it was when I was having a dawn cuppa and a bacon roll breakfast on the edge of Trafalgar Square that I met my husband.

I can see him now, strolling along the line of cabs, steaming mug in hand. ➜

"Have you ever been to Claridges?" he asked as we leaned on my taxi, talking shop in the sunrise.

"Yeah, you can pick up some good fares to the airport."

"I don't mean on the rank." He grinned. "I mean to dinner."

You get the odd drunk or someone who thinks they know the route better than you, but I've never had any real trouble," I tell Mr Handsome. "The worst I've heard about recently is a naughty boy who runs off without paying his fare."

Monkey Harris told me about it a few days ago when we were waiting on the rank at the Savoy. It hadn't happened to Monkey but an acquaintance of ours, Romford Ron.

"It's the third time I've heard it happen it in the last month," Monkey grumbled. "And always on the same run. It must be someone having a laugh."

"Surely someone got his face on camera?" I put in.

"Yeah, but it's no help if the bill don't know who they're looking for."

"If some ice cream bilked me, I'd have run after him and flattened him," opined Heart Attack, who was so named because of his sumo wrestler bulk.

"If you ran anywhere, you'd be in A&E!" Monkey laughed, uncharitably.

"You mustn't chase after them anyway," I cautioned. "It could be a decoy to get you out of your cab while someone else nicks your money bag. There must be something we can do, though."

Well, here we are: the White Duck." I pull up outside the restaurant after a journey in which we've barely had to pause at a set of lights.

"You deserve a good tip." Mr Handsome slides out a crocodile wallet as he opens his door.

He isn't dressed like a man who would need to cheat a cabbie, so I guess Monkey was right: he's just does it for a laugh. Because instead of leaning in the passenger window to pay, the tip he gives me is, "You can't trust anyone!"

Then he's up on his toes and running down the high street, his expensive coat flapping like a cape.

I jam my fist on the horn and two men block the pavement and grab the fare-dodger by each arm. Shades, parked on my rear bumper, runs over in case they need a hand to restrain him, but I think Monkey and my husband Big Al have the situation under control. Heart pounding, I breathe a sigh of relief as I dial 999.

I recognised Mr Handsome from Ron's CCTV footage as soon as he gave his destination. I messaged our specially set up social media group while he was climbing into the cab. I had no idea which, if any, of my colleagues would be in the vicinity to nab him, we'd just agreed that whoever was around if the alert went out would try to be there.

We cabbies look after each other, you see – and what's more, we don't like being taken for a ride. **MW**

MY INSPIRATION

I'm always fascinated by what goes on behind the scenes and the things the public doesn't see. *Sherbet Dab Ride* was inspired by a documentary on cabbies and I tried to get in all their slang and culture.

RECIPE AND FOOD STYLING: JENNIE SHAPTER PHOTOGRAPHY: JON WHITAKER

50
Calories per
square

Stem Ginger Fudge

Ingredients
(Makes 900g)

- ◆ **397g can condensed milk**
- ◆ **450g caster sugar**
- ◆ **50g butter, cut into pieces**
- ◆ **100ml milk**
- ◆ **2tbsp stem ginger syrup from the jar**
- ◆ **75g stem ginger in syrup, chopped**

1 Line a shallow 18cm tin with non-stick baking paper. Place the condensed milk, caster sugar, butter, milk and stem ginger syrup in a saucepan. Heat gently to dissolve the sugar.

2 Bring to the boil and boil steadily until it reaches 115°C (soft ball stage). Stir gently to stop the sugar from catching.

3 Remove from the heat and cool for 5min, then using an electric hand whisk, beat for about 5min, until thick and opaque. Stir in the chopped ginger and transfer to the prepared tin.

4 Allow to cool completely. Cut into squares and place in a box to give as a gift. Will keep for up to a month in an airtight container.

➜ **166**

Good Vibrations

When Sienna came into his life, Ross learned the true value of his guitars – and of his best friend's memory

By Tess Niland Kimber

Sienna loved her job, visiting a property that was past its best and then sprinkling her magic. She could turn a dirty, untidy house into a little palace in a few hours. Her clients like Mr Patel were always thrilled.

"Oh Miss Sienna, you have made me proud. The house – it look like new pin," he smiled.

He'd recently had a knee replacement and couldn't clean his flat, so he'd hired Sienna. The pay was good, but it was the smile on her clients' faces that was the real reward, she thought, unplugging her vacuum cleaner.

Sienna surveyed her handiwork. The red carpet was hoovered, the dining table polished and his newspapers tidied a spray of pink tulips from her large grey bag. "There!" she said, arranging the heavy blooms.

She'd hit on the idea when she'd started her cleaning business *Maid in the UK*. She didn't want to be a generic cleaner – all mop and buckets and hair in rollers. She wanted to be a modern domestic who looked after her appearance and whose business stood out from her competitors. So, she'd decided to leave flowers in each clients' property at the end of each visit. Of course, she'd always check first that they didn't suffer from pollen allergies or object.

So far everyone was thrilled with her finishing touch, she thought, slipping out of her white pumps and into the pink stilettoes she wore between appointments.

"I do not know how you can even step

She slipped on pink stilettoes, happy her client loved her pink tulips finishing touch

away. She'd also washed his crockery and bleached the bathroom.

"I'm glad you're pleased," she smiled. "Same time next week?"

"Please!"

Sienna nodded but there was one task to complete which set her apart from other cleaners in the area. Collecting a vase from Mr Patel's kitchen, she chose in those shoes, Miss Sienna," Mr Patel laughed as she picked up her bag and hoover to leave.

"You sound like my mum," she smiled. "Actually, I find them easier to walk in than flatties."

Sienna set off to a new client who'd an apartment in the block opposite. Mr Langstone had sounded ➡

desperate when he'd phoned to hire her.

"I work from home and can't get around to cleaning with my workload."

"No problem. *Maid in the UK* can always help," Sienna had smiled.

Ross Langstone was intrigued. Looking up from his computer, he saw the strangest sight through his basement window: a pair of turned-up jeans, pink stilettoes and whoever owned these shapely legs was carrying a large bag filled with tulips.

When his bell buzzed, he groaned. The new cleaner was due soon, but Jeans Girl had beaten her to it. No doubt she was a doorstep salesperson. He would buy her tulips as he couldn't turn people away.

"You're too polite, Ross," his mum

blonde wearing a pristine white t-shirt, turned up jeans with pink stilettoes, and carrying a bag of tulips. But it was her eyes that bewitched him. They were the most dazzling blue he'd ever seen.

Sienna smiled at the man who'd opened the door. He was about her age with a close-cropped beard and long wavy hair.

"Hello," she smiled, wondering if he was alright. He hadn't spoken and his mouth was slightly open.

Eventually he recovered the power of speech. "H… Hi. Sorry. Can I help…" he swallowed, "…you?"

"I'm Sienna – from *Maid in the UK*," she smiled, extending her hand.

Now that he'd closed his mouth, he really was quite good-looking, actually.

The guitar had belonged to his best friend and was his most treasured instrument

would say. "Say you're not interested. Assert yourself."

He'd pushed his hand through his dark hair. "But I feel so sorry for salespeople. Being self-employed I know it's hard to make a good living sometimes."

"But you've bought so much rubbish."

His mum was right. So far this year he'd bought a charcoal drawing of the marina with a seagull larger than the pub in the foreground, a stone Buddha for a garden he didn't have and a jar of pickled onions he'd never eat.

He left his cluttered desk and reluctantly answered the door, moving two prized guitars out of the way. Hopefully the new cleaner would soon arrive, giving him an excuse to extract himself from this caller.

Ross was still thinking how to keep the conversation short when he opened the door. On the step was a tall, willowy

When he still frowned, she added, "I'm your new cleaner. I'm guessing you're Mr Langstone."

"Sorry. Yes, I'm Ross. Please, come in. Sorry, I was expecting an… older lady."

"We cleaners come in all shapes and sizes. Think of Mrs Hinch," Sienna laughed but when he didn't show any recognition, she asked, "Now – where would you like me to start?"

Ross stopped staring and said, "The lounge please, but it's quite messy."

Sienna smiled. "Don't worry. I'll soon have it show house ready."

"Thank you. Would you like a drink?" he offered.

"Please – but when I've finished," she said, slipping out of her pink heels into her white pumps.

"Do you mind if I get on while you do? I work from home."

"Of course – please don't let me stop

you," Sienna said as he showed her into the lounge.

As he disappeared down the corridor, she thought, he wasn't wrong – the lounge was a mess! The sofa was covered in papers, there was a guitar on the floor being restrung with thin wires standing from the bridge like strands of hair and on the table were several dirty mugs.

However, she'd seen worse and soon set to work, tidying the papers and taking the cups out to the kitchen.

Here wasn't much better. Ross clearly needed a cleaner, she thought, as she loaded the sink. Suddenly she heard the most amazing sounds. She stopped to listen as if she'd been invited to a private rock concert…

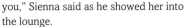

R oss strummed the first chord on his Gibson Les Paul guitar. The beautiful amber casing felt so comfortable in his arms. It was his most treasured instrument as it had belonged to his best friend Adam whose father, Brad, had gifted it to Ross five years ago.

He sighed, thinking of Adam as he played which had been Brad's intention.

"The music mustn't die with Adam…" Brad had tried to smile as he'd handed Ross the magnificent guitar. "You were his best friend and a musician too, so this seems right."

Ross was immensely touched and promised to cherish it, just as he did the memory of his dear friend.

Although he always played his best on this guitar he couldn't rely on good vibes; he must practise. He'd a gig later this month and the set list was complicated. He liked that though. A challenge.

But as he switched on his computer and adjusted the guitar's tuning, his mind wasn't on the notes. He could hear Sienna in the next room, moving, clinking cups, opening curtains. Sienna…

Of course, he always found it hard to work when he wasn't alone, but this was different. He was haunted by colours – dazzling blue and pale pink. The new cleaner really was a stunner. Adam wouldn't have wasted a moment asking her out.

He smiled thinking of his old friend. Tall, effortlessly cool, no girl was immune to his looks and charm. Adam wasn't a player though; he always respected his girlfriends.

"Treat every girl how you'd like your sister or mum romanced," he'd ➡

advise whenever Ross asked how he was so successful with girls. Yes, Adam had always been a gentleman but ultimately, it had killed him…

"Wow! This is awesome," Ross said, emerging from his bedroom.

"I'm glad you're pleased. I'll clean your room now if you like," Sienna offered.

He pulled a face. "Please be careful. I'm not being rude, but the last cleaner broke my Ibanez…"

"Ibanez?"

"It's a make of guitar," he explained. "Only, I need all my guitars in working order. I've a gig next month."

"I'll be careful," she promised, a little miffed he didn't trust her until she remembered they'd only just met so he was bound to be wary.

Pushing open his bedroom door, Sienna was amazed by all the equipment. Lining the walls were several guitars – some electric, some acoustic – his desk was dominated by a computer screen and by his bed was an amp, a mike stand, and a heap of cables. Surveying the room, she

repeated as they sat in his now gleaming kitchen. "Well, at uni I studied business but enjoyed cleaning more. Although, as it happens, the course helped a lot when I started working for myself."

"And you're doing well?"

"Oh yes, I've had to take on staff, actually. Business is booming."

"Or blooming…" he nodded towards the tulips.

She'd laughed and the image of her smile stayed long after she'd gone.

Sienna hadn't lied when she'd told Ross she loved her job. With the extra staff, she could easily run her business from home, but she loved client contact so ensured she cleaned the homes of her favourites. Like Mr Patel, Freda Clear and now of course, Ross Langstone.

As the weeks passed, she really got to know Ross. He was a beautiful man – outside and in.

As spring slipped into summer, they went on a couple of low-key dates.

When they'd shared their first kiss, Ross asked, "Is this allowed? A kiss

Adam would have told him, "No guitar is as important as the girl you love"

wasn't sure where to start but eventually, she brought order to the chaos, vacuuming the carpet and polishing his desk, while being super careful not to damage his prized guitars.

Ross gazed at the tulips in the milk canister – he didn't own a vase – but it wasn't the flowers haunting his thoughts, it was Sienna. He'd never met a girl like her. She was not only beautiful, she was interesting as well, as he'd discovered when they'd shared a coffee.

"How did I get into cleaning?" she'd

between employer and employee?"

"Well, I think as long as the employee and employer are happy, it's totally permissible," she'd laughed as the evening sun set. "But maybe we need another kiss to be absolutely sure?"

Sienna felt so happy. She'd a job she loved and was dating Ross who was great. What could go wrong?

Ross was stressed. The Reading gig was in two days. Although he'd the set list down and had arranged transport with the band's drummer, he was still busy.

Thankfully Sienna was here to spruce up the flat.

"Honestly Ross, how do you manage to get it so messy?"

"I do it on purpose – just so you'll stay longer."

She laughed as she dragged the vacuum down the hall to his bedroom.

"Be…"

"…careful! Yes, I know," she said, opening the door and thinking it looked more untidy than usual.

Although some equipment was packed ready for the gig tomorrow, his guitars – especially his prized Gibson Les Paul – were still on floor stands. Sighing, she tidied some cables and then vacuumed under the bed.

As she changed the hoover head, she noticed a plectrum under the desk. Bending to pick it up, she lost her balance as she'd forgotten to change out of her pink stilettoes. She tried to steady herself but knocked a guitar stand, hitting her elbow. There was a sickening bang and she watched in horror as Ross's favourite guitar fell…

"Sienna!" he shouted from the doorway as she righted both herself and the guitar.

"I'm so sorry… I… sorry…" she said, rubbing her arm.

"I asked you to be careful around my guitars," he frowned.

"Is… is it OK?" she asked.

"If it is, it's no thanks to you," he muttered, examining the Gibson Les Paul.

Suddenly Sienna felt angry. He hadn't even asked if she was OK or acknowledged her apology. With tears stinging, she stood up, holding her sore arm.

"I think it's time I left," she said.

As soon as he heard the flat door slam, Ross regretted his angry words. How could he have spoken like that to Sienna? His Sienna…

He rushed down the hallway and pulled open the front door.

"Sienna!" he called but she'd already driven off.

Feeling utterly miserable, he picked up his mobile phone. He wouldn't call as she was driving, so he sent a text:

I'm so sorry. Call me. Please.

Unable to believe what he'd done, he picked up the Gibson Les Paul. Stroking the amber guitar, he double checked it for damage. This model had a weak headstock but luckily it was fine.

Why had he over-reacted like that? Of course, he was stressed about the gig, and he was over-protective as this had been Adam's guitar, but that was no real excuse.

As he strummed the guitar, he imagined his dear friend saying, "Treat girls as you'd want your mum or sister to be romanced."

Adam had always looked after his girlfriends. What would he say if he was here? He'd probably tell him off, saying, "No guitar is as important as the girl you love, Ross."

As he wondered how to apologise, Ross suddenly had a good idea…

Sienna was in tears when she arrived home. How could she have been so clumsy? Not only had she upset Ross, she could have damaged his prized guitar which had once belonged to his best friend, Adam. ➤

As she bathed her bad arm, she wondered how Adam had died. She didn't like to ask Ross. After drying her arm, she checked her phone and found an apologetic text from Ross. She smiled. Suddenly there was a knock at the door.

"Ross!"

"Sienna," he said, looking stricken as he held out the spray of tulips she'd left at his flat. "I'm so sorry. I shouldn't have shouted. These are for you."

"Me?"

"Yes… you give everyone flowers, but you deserve them, too."

She smiled. "Thanks Ross."

"Are you OK?"

"I hit my elbow, but it's just bruised."

"Can I see?"

She showed him and he gently kissed it. "Better?"

"Lots," she smiled. "Come in."

She showed him into the kitchen where she put the tulips into a vase.

"I'm sorry. No guitar's worth more than you."

"Not even Adam's Gibson Les Paul?" she searched his dark eyes.

"Not even Adam's guitar… It's funny I still think of it as his," he said, sadly.

Tentatively Sienna touched his arm. "That's good. It means he's still here in some way… You never said what happened…"

Ross took a deep breath, "It still hurts – that's why I got so upset over the guitar. He got hit by a car."

"Oh no!" Sienna covered her mouth.

"You see, Adam was the perfect gentleman. Held doors open for people, gave up his seat on the bus, pulled out chairs for girls."

"Wow! People don't often have manners like that anymore," she said.

"No, they don't, and I wish every day that Adam hadn't had them either."

When she frowned, he added, "If he hadn't been such a gentleman, he wouldn't have stepped aside for a mum pushing a pram. As he did so he fell off the kerb into the path of the car. It was no one's fault but if he hadn't moved for the woman, he'd still be here."

"That's so tragic."

"I miss him every day. It's why his guitar means so much."

She hugged him. "I understand. I'm sorry I almost broke it."

"Don't be. Today when I checked the guitar, I sensed Adam telling me you're more important than any guitar. If he was here, he'd be more worried about you than the guitar. As I should have been."

He kissed her.

"You know," she said, when they finally moved apart. "Adam sounds like a wonderful person."

"He was," Ross agreed. "Like you are. And he does live on. It sounds mad but earlier, I felt him. Guiding me. Bringing us back together."

As she snuggled into his arms, she silently thanked Adam. Somehow, she doubted they'd need his help again. Not now they valued each other too much to let anything come between them again. Ⓜ️Ⓦ

MY INSPIRATION

Many of my stories are inspired by my three children. My eldest son Patrick, who's a musician, sparked this story. I'm his "roadie" and he's always worried I'll damage his guitars. That gave me a "What If…?" moment.

The Pea Soup Fiasco

The aimless Laura and shy Sue discover they have talents after all – and all because of the pea soup!

By Barbara Dynes

B reak-time at the café where I work. Sipping coffee, I think about my life. *Laura, you are guy-less, homeless and goal-less*, I tell myself. Goal-less means I've never been that fussed about "getting on in life", as my mother puts it. Any ambition to be a celebrity, brain surgeon or whatever, just passed me by. No doubt I've missed out, big time. Yet I really like this job.

"Oh, I'm sorry, sir!" I hear a panicked voice from across the room.

I groan. Sounds like Sue, our new temp, has hit the disaster button again. I hurry across to where an agitated gent is glaring at a pool of spilt coffee and manage to calm him down, while a flustered Sue mops the table. Luckily, our boss, Jessie, is out.

I had my doubts about Sue after Jessie took her on the other day. A nice enough woman, but she didn't know ➡

a cappuccino from a latte, plus she's a bit shy with customers.

Anyway, I've other things to worry about. Such as my Darren finding a new love a while back. I cried a river, as they say, and that river has still not quite dried up, to be honest. Then, of course, me and the gorgeous Mr Jones had to move out of Darren's flat. I found us another, but now I've been given two weeks' notice to quit this one. The landlord has me down as a cat smuggler. OK, the small print did say no domestic pets, but we were desperate, me and my ginger Jonesy.

Now, I go to console a red-faced Sue.

"You're doing fine, love!"

I put my arm around her, then frown. Who am I calling "love"? Sue's around my age, mid-twenties and single, like me. I feel for her – and she was so grateful yesterday, when I gave her a lift home. Trying to be friendly, I tell her about Mr Jones and my own plight.

narrowly avoids a lap full of green high-fibre liquid, served by Sue, our new assistant realises the game is up.

"Thank you, Laura, for being so kind," is Sue's parting shot to me. "Do come and have a cuppa one day."

I warm to her; she seems really lonely, and, on my next day off, fed up with driving round town looking for flats that welcome cats, I decide to take her up on that invite.

Sue's place is cosy, with lots of books and flowers around.

"I do hope you get another job soon," I say, over coffee.

She doesn't answer that but, later, she picks up her jacket.

"Come for a walk," she says. "I've something to show you."

Ten minutes later, Sue unlocks the door to a small ground floor flat.

"A friend has just moved out. The

An elegantly-dressed woman narrowly avoids a lap full of green high-fibre liquid

Next day, there is another calamity and this time the boss is watching. Sue only plonks vegetarian mushroom risotto in front of Big Jeff, a regular from the building site. His usual bangers and mash go to fussy little Miss Harley. Jeff, glued to the snooker on the wall telly, has wolfed down most of the mushrooms before Miss H signals her distress. As he's not complaining and he only gets half an hour for lunch, I tell him to carry on eating, consoling Miss H with another Earl Grey while she awaits her fresh risotto.

"My fault entirely, that mix-up," I inform Jessie later, winking at Sue as she tries to protest. And we get away with it.

But it all ends with a pea soup fiasco. After an elegantly-dressed woman

rent's reasonable and there's even a patch of garden for your Mr Jones."

Wow, this is too good to be true!

As Sue shows me around, I ask what she considers a reasonable rent and, unbelievably, it's a fair bit less than I'm paying now.

"Perfect! Where can I find the landlord?"

"That's me," she says quietly.

"You? "

"I write, actually. Made a bit of money with my last book, added it to my savings and bought this as an investment. Cressida Curtis is my pen-name."

I blink. Sue is only a real-life author! I feel bad that I don't know her writing name, but then I'm no reader.

What I definitely am, though, is completely overawed. Even our shy Sue seems to have got somewhere in life! Unlike yours truly.

"But the cafe job? " I query.

"Research. The heroine in my new book owns a restaurant."

"Ah, I get it! And I'm really glad we met because this flat will be great," I add.

Sue hesitates.

"Laura…" she starts. "Would you help me with my book?"

"Me, help you?" I repeat incredulously.

"Well, yes, because you're so good at your job, you see – and with people. You could certainly teach me a thing or two." Sue smiles. "Writing is a lonely business,

actually. I do hope we can be friends?"

I nod vigorously. "You must come and meet Mr Jones!" Suddenly, I feel so much better. Maybe, as Sue – or Cressida – says, I do have a talent, after all. Kindness and being a people person has its own rewards. And, who knows, Sue might even get me reading books… 🅼🆆

Spirit of Place

Supernatural communicator Natalie may need a little assistance to lift the atmosphere of gloom

By Linda Lewis

Mr Matthews peered over Natalie's shoulder as if expecting the cast of the Ghostbusters film to be following her down the path.

"Are you the ghost shifter?" he asked.

"That's me," Natalie said.

"Where's all your equipment?"

"It's all in here." She lifted her briefcase. Her client didn't move.

"Do you want to show me where the problem is, Mr Matthews?"

"If you don't get rid of the ghost, I don't have to pay anything. Is that right?" he demanded. "Only you're not the first person who's tried."

Natalie smiled. She wasn't after money.

"I don't charge a fee. All I ask is a donation to my favourite charity. Maybe you should try someone else."

She turned to leave.

"Wait! Now you're here, you may as well look. The problem's in the dining room."

He strode off so quickly, Natalie had to run to keep up with him.

It was a shame he was such a grump. He'd be attractive if he smiled…

She pushed the thought away. She'd given up on romance when her boyfriend moved on to pastures new.

After leading her through a gloomy kitchen with slate-grey walls, Mr Matthews stopped in a doorway.

"So – what do you think, then?"

As soon as Natalie stepped into the

room, she felt a presence. Happily it wasn't angry or dangerous; instead it felt sad.

"I sense a spirit of some kind. Have you felt anything?"

"Of course not," he replied. "My late wife said we had a ghost but I never saw it. I don't believe any of this nonsense. I only contacted you because I'm selling the house. So far, I've had no offers. People say the place is haunted."

Natalie found it hard not to smile. He looked so annoyed, as though the ghost was being difficult on purpose. She closed her eyes for a moment and concentrated.

"There's definitely something here. The good news is that it seems to be benign."

"Great," he said briskly. "So – can you get rid of it or not?"

"I'll certainly do my best," she replied. He nodded.

"In that case, I'll leave you to it." Not even an offer of a cup of tea.

Something about his manner told her that he wasn't being rude intentionally. It was probably his way of coping with the loss of his wife.

She was unpacking her gear, which consisted mainly of recording equipment, when the ghost spoke to her.

"You won't need any of that," he said.

Natalie was so startled, she almost screamed. She took a deep breath.

"Good morning," she said, cautiously. "My name's Natalie Pearson, and you are?"

"Henry Seymour Aldwych the Third. ➡

Delighted to make your acquaintance."
As he spoke, a shadowy figure appeared, dressed in Edwardian clothes. It was as if his body had been carved out of air.

"You can see me," he said. "Most people can't even hear me. I'm impressed."

Natalie didn't know what to say. She'd never been in a situation like this. Normally, she'd be lucky to catch a glimpse of a spirit.

"What do you make of Mr Sourpuss?" the ghost asked.

"He seems sad," she replied. "It's a shame. If he lost that frown, he'd be very good looking."

"He hasn't smiled since his wife died," Henry explained. "For months afterwards, he was more like a ghost than I am. His wife was a wonderful woman. I was happy when

"There's nothing to be scared of," she said softly. "You need to move on. That's the way it works."

"I know," Henry replied, "but I can't. Believe me I've tried, many times."

"How's it going? Have you got rid of it?" Mr Matthews was in the doorway. The ghost had vanished.

"You made me jump!" Natalie said.

He gave her a thin smile which went nowhere hear his eyes. "And you a ghost shifter. Maybe you're in the wrong job."

Natalie counted to ten, slowly. It wasn't a job to her, she did it for love.

"There's a problem," she explained. "The ghost is scared to leave. He has agoraphobia."

"And you know this how?"

He shuddered. "I haven't left these four walls for a hundred and thirty years"

she was here. She wasn't scared of me, like most people are. You're not scared, are you?" he demanded.

"Not at all," she said, realising it was true. "So, Henry. What's keeping you here?"

"I'm too frightened to leave."

"What are you scared of? Nothing bad can happen. You're already dead."

"I haven't left these four walls for a hundred and thirty years." He looked round the room and shuddered. "I couldn't leave the house when I was alive. Being dead hasn't made any difference."

"You poor soul," she said. "It sounds as if you're suffering from agoraphobia."

"What's that?" Henry enquired.

"Fear of open spaces," she explained gently. "It's usually brought on by some kind of trauma. Did you have an accident?"

He nodded. "I fell from my horse, nearly died. I haven't left the house since."

Natalie tried to touch his arm to comfort him. Her hand went right through.

"Because he told me about it."

Mr Matthews laughed. "Of course. Silly me. So, can you get rid of it or not?"

"I'm not sure. If I can contact another spirit, they might be able to convince Henry to leave with them."

"Can't 'Henry' speak to another ghost without your help?"

Again Natalie bristled; he'd said Henry's name as though it was a curse.

"He could, but there aren't any other ghosts here."

"And without their help, he can't leave. I can understand that." His frown changed into a scowl. "Do whatever you need to. The sooner I sell this place the better."

"There's another problem," Natalie explained. "I can't do it alone, it's too dangerous. Would you be able to help me?"

He shook his head. "Sorry. No."

"That's fine." She picked up her case. "I'll have to come back."

Mr Matthews sighed.

"Hang on. If I agree to help you, do you really think you can make the ghost leave?"

"I certainly hope so," she replied.

"Right then. Let's get on with it." He sat down at the desk.

"We need to hold hands," she said, "to concentrate the energy."

As their fingers touched, a jolt of electricity ran up her arm. From the look on his face, he'd felt it too, but his frown soon reappeared.

"I need to go into a trance, so that a spirit can speak through me. Could you close your eyes too?"

"Whatever," he replied.

Immediately the ghost appeared.

"You like him, don't you?"

"Sssh!" she whispered. "He'll hear you."

"I didn't say anything," replied Mr Matthews crossly.

"I didn't mean you. I was talking to the ghost. To Henry."

"It's fine. He can't hear me," explained Henry. "So what happens now?"

"I'm going to try to contact a spirit who's passed over safely so you can talk to them."

"What for?" snapped Mr Matthews. "That's your job. I don't want to talk to any spirits, thank you very much."

Natalie sighed.

"I'm talking to Henry," she said again.

She closed her eyes and after taking seven deep breaths, relaxed into a trance.

"Is there anyone there who can help this lost spirit move on?"

Silence. She tried again. "I'm with Henry Aldwych. He's afraid to leave and needs your help. Please, can anyone hear me?"

A sudden jolt shook her body as a spirit took over her.

"I'm happy to try," said a woman's voice.

"Sylvia – is that you?" gasped Mr Matthews.

"Yes, darling. It's me."

"I miss you. So, so much."

"I know, and I miss you too, but I'm at peace now. You need to move on, sweetheart. Find love again."

Mr Matthews got up and stormed out, snapping Natalie out of her trance.

"What happened?"

The ghost chuckled. "The spirit you contacted was only his dead wife, Sylvia."

After a lengthy pause, he sighed but it wasn't a sad sound, it was heavy with relief.

"She's here with me now. With her help, I think I can leave. Goodbye, Natalie. Thank you so much."

Moments later, the atmosphere changed. There would be no more problems with ghosts here.

She found Mr Matthews in the neglected garden, standing stiffly, staring into the distance.

"The ghost has moved on now," she told him softly.

He turned towards her, his eyes blazing.

"That was a really cheap trick, conjuring up my late wife."

Not wanting an argument, Natalie walked away. "Goodbye, Mr Matthews. If you could send a donation to the charity, that would be great."

It had been a long time since she'd felt such a strong connection to a man. It was a shame they hadn't met in different circumstances. She would have liked to get to know him better.

The next time she drove past, the For Sale sign had gone. ➡

Six weeks later, he called her. "Is that Natalie Pearson? The ghost shifter?"

"Yes. Speaking."

"Good. It's Damien Matthews. Can you come round sometime?"

"Of course. Did the ghost come back?"

"No. Look, I'll explain when you get here."

She arranged to call at the house on her way home from work that evening.

She hardly recognised him. He looked completely different, much more relaxed. He was smiling too.

"Thanks for coming," he said. "Can I get you something to drink? "

"I'd love a coffee. Thanks."

When she followed him into the kitchen, she gasped. The dark walls were now a sunny shade of yellow.

"Wow!" she said. "What a difference."

He chuckled. "It's not just the kitchen," Natalie noticed a hint of pride in his voice. "Let's have these in the garden."

As he opened the back door Natalie"s jaw dropped. The long grass and tangled weeds had gone, the overgrown borders were neat and tidy and new shrubs had been planted.

He led her to a new summer house.

"Wow," she said as she sat on a comfortable bench. "You've done an amazing job. This will add thousands to the value of the house."

"It would, but I'm not selling." He put the mugs down on a mosaic-topped table. "I wanted to apologise for the way I behaved last time we met. I also wanted to thank you for this."

He waved a hand to indicate the garden. "I don't know if that scene in the dining room was real or staged –" Natalie tried to interrupt but he stopped her. "The point is, it doesn't matter. It made me stop and think. This house was Sylvia's project. We'd planned to work on it together, but before we could start, she became ill.

"After she died, two years ago, I lost heart. I felt stuck, rather like that ghost of yours. Thanks to you, I've decided to stay here and make new memories. It's what Sylvia would have wanted." He paused and she noticed he was looking at her differently, as if he'd never really seen her before and liked what he saw.

"This is difficult," he admitted. "Will you have dinner with me sometime? There. Now you can shoot me down in flames."

Natalie didn't need to think about it.

"I'd love to," she said.

MY INSPIRATION

All kinds of things inspire my writing. Some of my favourites are animals, especially dogs, and unusual jobs or hobbies. If I can throw some romance into the mix, that's always a bonus.

Brain Boosters

Kriss Kross

Turn To Page 157 For Solutions

Try to fit all the listed words back into the grid.

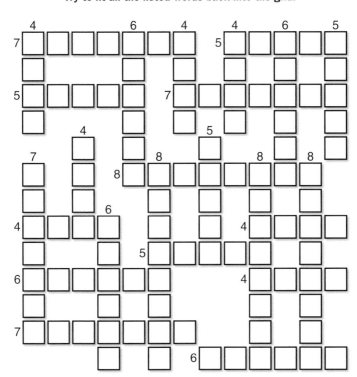

4 letters	5 letters	6 letters	7 letters	8 letters
Amen	Inlet	Ascend	Brinjal	Audition
Bash	Locum	Chorus	Develop	Ecstatic
Lard	Miser	Goblet	Nervous	Lameness
Lino	Regal	Joyful	Unwaged	Spaceman
Slab	Story	Pollen		
Whip				
Yogi				

Just Name That Tune

It took a hospital DJ and entertainer to make Tristan see the value of what was right in front of him

By **Jenny Worstall**

"I should be conducting at the Albert Hall," Tristan Chord said to the nurse attending to his leg, "not stuck on a hospital ward. The concert started ten minutes ago."

"Never mind, Mr Chord," the nurse said as she finished applying the dressing. "They were lucky to get that famous young conductor to step in at the last minute, weren't they?"

Tristan sighed. He probably wouldn't even be missed this afternoon at the concert. What's more, he had only had one visitor while he had been in hospital – Debbie Damson, his next-door neighbour.

A bell rang for the end of visiting time and scores of families and friends left the ward, waving to their loved ones.

"Think I'll have a snooze now," Tristan muttered as he closed his eyes and rolled his head from side to side on the pillow, ruffling what was left of his hair.

An image of Debbie's kindly face blossomed unbidden in his mind, her friendly smile, her wide-set eyes, blue as cornflowers, and the soft coral-coloured cardigan she had been wearing when she'd rescued him. ➜

The accident had happened a few days ago. Tristan had been pottering about in his garden when he'd noticed his windows weren't looking their best.

"Need a jolly good clean," he puffed as he looked up at the dull glass. "Won't take me long to get the telescopic ladder out and get them shining again."

The window cleaning went just about as badly as it could have, with Tristan falling from a considerable height into a prickly rose bed, a bucket of warm soapy water landing on his head. After yelling for help for several minutes, he was on the point of giving up when Debbie's head popped over the top of the wicker fence.

"Dear me! I'll be with you in a flash. You should have done a risk assessment before you started on those windows, Tristan!"

She squeezed through a narrow gap to get access to his garden.

"Just as well I'm slim!" she said.

A closer look at Tristan had her reaching for her mobile. He was breathing

"I'm not Tristan's wife – I'm Miss Debbie Damson. But I'll make sure he has everything he needs. Thank you, Doctor."

Over the next few days, Debbie had visited Tristan every day, keeping him comfortable with his favourite toiletries, fresh night clothes and plenty to read.

The hospital tea trolley rattling down the ward woke Tristan from his slumber. "Cup of tea, Mr Chord?" asked Eva, one of the catering staff.

"Don't mind if I do," he replied. "Got any Lapsang Souchong? Earl Grey?"

"Not today," Eva replied. "Today it's black or white. Same as yesterday."

"I live in hope," Tristan said. "White. Three sugars."

"Goodness me, Mr Chord, what very lovely pyjamas you are wearing – are those tiny pianos embroidered onto the collar?" Eva leaned forward.

"Yes, musical PJs," Tristan replied. "Customised for me by my neighbour, Debbie. She brought them in yesterday."

Tristan flapped his hand at the ridiculous notion of Debbie having feelings for him

erratically and his leg was sticking out at a funny angle.

"I feel weird," he muttered, before passing out momentarily – and then throwing up.

In no time at all, Tristan was in the safe hands of the professionals, with the diagnosis of a badly broken leg, extensive cuts and bruises all over his body, and a touch of concussion for good measure.

"You definitely need an operation on that leg, plus quite a few nights staying with us," the doctor said. "Is there anyone who can collect a few bits and pieces for you from home? Ah, good. Thank you, Mrs Chord."

"What very fine stitching, it must have taken her ages! She certainly thinks a lot of you, then."

"Women like doing this sort of thing, don't they?" Tristan flapped his hand as if conducting a rapid passage of music and wafted the ridiculous notion of Debbie Damson having feelings for him out of his mind.

Eva shook her head as she continued on her way down the ward.

Suddenly the swing doors flew open and a young man burst in, laden with an enormous amplifier, a keyboard and sheaves of music.

"Harry Warbler's the name," he

announced as he parked himself near the end of the ward, right next to Tristan's bed, "And music's the game. I've come to cheer you all up! Now, any requests?"

"Good grief," muttered Tristan. "This must be what the nurse was babbling on about this morning, about how some volunteer would be coming round to get us all singing."

"He's ever so good," the man in the next bed confided. "A musical genius on the keyboard and he does programmes on hospital radio too."

Very soon all the patients, apart from Tristan, were having a really good go at joining in with the songs from the shows. *Supercalifragilisticexpialidocious, Climb Every Mountain* and *A Spoon full of Sugar* echoed through the ward and beyond. In the end even Tristan found his toes itching to tap in time, despite being battered and bruised.

"That's all I've got time for – thanks for listening, guys," Harry shouted as he packed away his keyboard. "See you all again soon!"

"Not if I can help it," Tristan retorted.

"Tristan," a passing nurse said, "That was most ungracious."

"I only meant I hope I'll be going home soon," Tristan said.

He pulled the covers a little higher over himself and felt ashamed. Maybe Debbie would come and visit soon.

Debbie was at that moment letting herself into Tristan's house. She needed to collect a few more things for him and was happy to be useful. She was, in fact, devoted to Tristan and had been for many years, but she suspected she didn't even appear on his radar except as someone to feed his cat, take his parcels in and keep an eye on the rubbish bins when he was

touring with his orchestra. Debbie bit her lip, thinking of all the glamorous lady musicians he must meet on his travels. She crept past his untidy music room, dominated by a vast black beast of a piano decorated with empty coffee cups and pieces of music, then up the stairs to his bedroom.

Tristan hadn't said much about the pair of pyjamas she'd embroidered – but he had looked very handsome wearing them.

She looked around to find the opera book he'd requested. Ah, there it was! Averting her eyes from the king-size bed, she grabbed the volume and fled.

Tristan's cat meowed plaintively as he saw Debbie.

"Siegfried, there you are! Not long now – Tristan will be home before ➤

you know it." Siegfried rubbed against her leg and she caressed his soft fur until he purred like an old-fashioned steam train.

Debbie Damson was one of the first visitors the next afternoon and Tristan was inordinately pleased to hear her heels echoing down the ward.

"Here's the book you asked for," Debbie said, handing over a large tome with a picture of a statuesque lady singing her heart out and wearing a full length garment a bit like a nightie, but with a golden belt. She had lashings of eye make-up, waist-length hair, and a fearsome-looking helmet with horns.

Just then, applause started as Harry Warbler appeared and took a bow.

"Harry Warbler's the name and –"

"Music's the game," Tristan said. "Yes, we know. Heard it before."

"Now," Harry said, "Today I'm going to make a request. I'm going to ask one of the greatest conductors in the country –"

Tristan had trouble sleeping that evening, what with the over-heated ward, myriad snorers disturbing the peace, and on top of that, feeling generally uncomfortable with so many injuries.

"I've brought you a cup of tea," a nurse whispered as she opened the curtain round Tristan's bed at eleven o'clock. "I could hear you tossing and turning. Perhaps you'd like to listen to our hospital radio? Harry Warbler has a late evening programme until midnight. Here, I'll help you set the volume. You might enjoy it."

"Harry Warbler? No, not at all, not my sort of music!"

"Mr Chord! We all think very highly of Harry and admire the way he's prepared to give up his time for others."

"Sorry! Forgive a grumpy old man?"

The nurse went into peals of laughter. "Grumpy – yes, but Mr Chord, you can't possibly consider yourself old. You see Fred, there, in the bed opposite, with his curtain open? Don't worry, he can't

"You're being unforgivably rude," Debbie told him before she left

"The world." Tristan interrupted.

"– to help me out with my show this afternoon. Mr Chord, would you do me the very great honour of conducting while I play my keyboard?"

"Afraid I can't help you," Tristan said. "Debbie, pull the curtains round my bed."

"Tristan," Debbie whispered. "You're being unforgivably rude. What is wrong with you? Don't you want to share your musical talents?"

"No!"

"Here you are," Debbie said as she dumped fresh clothes on the bed. "I'm not sure if I'll have the time to visit again."

"Debbie, wait, I'm sorry," Tristan called out. But she had gone.

hear us because he's got his earphones in listening to Harry Warbler. Well, he's ninety nine."

"Bet he'll go home before me."

"Doubt it," the nurse said. "You're well on the mend. Now, let's adjust your headset so it's nice and comfy."

"And next," Harry Warbler said, directly into Tristan's ears, "After that spectacular piece from the James Bond movie sung by Adele, I'd like to play the opening of Beethoven's Fifth Symphony. I'm dedicating this to Tristan Chord, the famous conductor, who we are honoured to have in our hospital this week. Hope he's listening – this one's for you, Tristan!"

Tristan sat up in bed and conducted

the familiar dramatic opening of one of his favourite pieces in delight as the nurse melted away, her job done.

Tristan settled down and tried to sleep but found his mind constantly replaying the regrettable scene when he had been so rude to Harry.

"Debbie must think I'm very selfish" he groaned. "Perhaps she won't visit again?"

He curled his fists into tight angry balls and wondered why he even minded what Debbie thought of him. Then, although it was difficult, he spent some time trying to imagine what it was like to be Debbie, always happy to help out with any chores he asked her to do and never asking for anything in return.

"I'm such an idiot!" he shouted out in the early hours as the scales finally fell from his eyes. "I care for Debbie, in fact, I'm falling in love with her!"

"Shh, there," the nurse soothed as she approached Tristan's bed. "Bad dream?"

"Not at all!" Tristan grinned then fell into a deep sleep, happier and more hopeful than he had been for a long time.

A couple of days later, Tristan was sitting up in bed reading when the nurse came to take his blood pressure.

"All good," she said. "Now let's take a look at your leg. Could you move your book? My word, that looks interesting. An opera called Tristan! So that's how you were blessed with such an unusual name."

"Yes. My parents were huge opera fans." Tristan wriggled about, trying to get more comfortable. "Of course, I was teased mercilessly at school."

"I expect you coped admirably," the nurse said, "With your strong personality!"

Tristan laughed. "How much longer do you think I'll be here for?"

"The doctor will decide when she's done her rounds, but I think you'll be leaving soon. We'll miss you!"

"Hello," a voice said.

"Harry!" Tristan was surprised to see the young man standing next to his bed. "What on earth have you done?"

"Fell over running for a bus while carrying my keyboard," Harry explained. "Cracked my head on the pavement and broke my arm into the bargain. Hadn't planned on coming back to hospital so soon and certainly not as a patient, but here I am."

"And here you'll stay for a night, just to keep an eye on that head injury," the nurse said.

"The thing is, Mr Chord," Harry began, "I wondered whether you might…"

"Of course!" Tristan roared. "Be delighted to, old fellow."

"But I haven't actually said what it is I would like you to help with," Harry said.

"I'm very intuitive," Tristan remarked. "I know exactly what you want me to do. You can't possibly play the keyboard with a broken arm and you want me to help you out by playing the accompaniment so your gig can go with a swing."

"Wow! That's it exactly," Harry said. "I'd be so grateful."

"Thanks for playing Beethoven's Fifth for me on your radio show – I was chuffed to bits," Tristan said, "And many apologies for my extremely boorish ➡

behaviour before."

"Forgotten already."

"Why don't we have a go at making music now?" Tristan suggested. "I know you usually do your cabaret later in the week, but what's stopping us?"

"Go for it!" Harry whooped.

"I'll set the keyboard up," the nurse offered, "And plug in the amplifier."

"Warbler and Chord's the name," Tristan bellowed down the ward, "And music's our game!"

Within minutes, everyone was singing and some of the nurses were even dancing.

"Bring me sunshine, in your smile," they sang.

Debbie could hear the rumpus as she came up the stairs. On entering the ward her heart raced to see her beloved Tristan propped up at the keyboard with his broken leg stretched out awkwardly.

"Bring me fun, Bring me sunshine, Bring me love," he sang, looking directly into her sparkling eyes.

Harry Warbler improvised a wonderful encore in the style of a rap at the end of the session. Tristan accompanied him on the keyboard. He was quite out of his usual comfort zone but thoroughly enjoying every minute of it.

"We'll do this again?" Harry asked.

"You bet!" Tristan replied.

A few weeks later, Debbie sat on Tristan's sofa, cradling a coffee.

"That was a delicious meal, Tristan," she said. "I didn't know you could cook."

"I've learnt a lot recently," he said, "Mostly about how to treat people – thanks to you."

"Me? You can't have learnt anything from me – I'm just an ordinary person," Debbie said, blushing.

"You are not ordinary," Tristan said.

"You are the most extra-ordinary person I have ever met. You've even taught me something about music."

Debbie looked puzzled. "Whatever do you mean?"

"Well, I used to get stuck on the third note of the scale."

"You've lost me!" Debbie said, her eyebrows knitting together.

"You know, the notes of the scale – remember when we sang the song from the *Sound of Music* with Harry Warbler?"

Tristan threw his head back and sang in his rich baritone voice…

"Doe, a deer, a female deer, Ray, a drop of golden sun, Me, a name I call myself… you know how it goes."

Debbie nodded as it dawned on her, and she started giggling as she began to understand what Tristan was actually talking about.

"You mean you couldn't move on from the 'me' bit?" she asked.

"Yes, it's been me, me, me, all my life, and that's been lonely."

"It's never too late," Debbie said, holding out her arms.

"Well, I can promise you that it isn't going to be me, me, me anymore," Tristan murmured, as he drew her into his arms. "It'll be you and me from now on." **MW**

MY INSPIRATION

My writing has always been inspired by my wonderful friends and family, music of all kinds, romantic love, little snippets of conversation I overhear – and a tendency not to take life too seriously!

Brain Boosters SOLUTIONS

CODEWORD FROM PAGE 37
PHRASE: DAVID MITCHELL AND ROBERT WEBB

M	O	S	Q	U	I	T	O		A	L	A	R	M
	S		U		D		L		L		N		A
D	E	C	E	I	V	E		I	L	L	E	G	A	L
I		I		Z		N		V		E		E		A
S	E	L	F		T	R	I	G	G	E	R	E	D
P		L		T		I		A		I				J
A	L	A	C	R	I	T	Y		G	A	T	E	A	U
S		T		A		Y		S		N		X		S
S	E	E	I	N	G		S	T	O	C	K	P	O	T
I			S		S		A		E		L			M
O	U	T	S	P	O	K	E	N		B	O	R	E
N		W		L		A		D		O		S		N
A	D	A	M	A	N	T		I	M	P	R	I	N	T
T		N		N		E		N		U		V	
E	I	G	H	T		D	I	G	E	S	T	E	D

KRISS KROSS FROM PAGE 149

B	R	I	N	J	A	L		L	O	C	U	M
A		O		I		A		H		I		
S	T	O	R	Y		N	E	R	V	O	U	S
H		F		O		D		R		E	
	Y		U		R		U		R	
U		O		L	A	M	E	N	E	S	S	
N		G		U		G		C		P	
W	H	I	P		D		A		S	L	A	B
A		O		I	N	L	E	T		C	
G	O	B	L	E	T		A	M	E	N	
E		L		I			T		M	
D	E	V	E	L	O	P		I		A	
	N		N		A	S	C	E	N	D	

MISSING LINK FROM PAGE 67
ACROSS: 7 Cement **8** Arable **9** Dial **10** Accident **11** Recognition **14** Regulations **18** Imperial **19** Year **20** Beetle **21** Earned
DOWN: 1 Devices **2** Deal **3** Strain **4** Mascot **5** Tandoori **6** Flint **12** Omelette **13** Engaged **15** United **16** Asleep **17** Umber **19** York
SHADED WORD: EDITOR

MISSING LINK FROM PAGE 87
ACROSS: 7 Gossip **8** Enough **9** Beta **10** Retainer **11** Territorial **14** Application **18** Nitrogen **19** Rage **20** Desert **21** Oxygen
DOWN: 1 Powered **2** Asia **3** Spirit **4** Sector **5** Dominant **6** Agree **12** Reporter **13** Goggles **15** Lights **16** Cannon **17** Lines **19** Rays
SHADED WORD: HEDGES

SUDOKU 1 FROM PAGE 111

5	1	9	3	4	6	8	7	2
4	6	7	2	5	8	9	1	3
2	8	3	7	1	9	5	4	6
3	7	4	8	2	5	1	6	9
1	5	8	9	6	4	2	3	7
9	2	6	1	3	7	4	8	5
7	9	5	4	8	3	6	2	1
6	4	2	5	7	1	3	9	8
8	3	1	6	9	2	7	5	4

SUDOKU 2 FROM PAGE 111

8	6	2	7	5	9	1	4	3
1	9	7	8	4	3	2	6	5
4	5	3	2	6	1	9	7	8
7	4	9	1	8	5	3	2	6
3	1	6	9	2	7	8	5	4
5	2	8	4	3	6	7	1	9
2	3	4	5	1	8	6	9	7
6	7	5	3	9	2	4	8	1
9	8	1	6	7	4	5	3	2

WORD WHEEL FROM PAGE 111 The nine-letter word is GROTESQUE

Sue's The Name

Who did our evacuee think she was, stealing and breaking our things? Lessons needed to be learned...

By Barbara Dynes

We're going to take in an evacuee, Susie. We need to help get children away from London and all the bombing – give one of them a home," Mum explained.

I understood that, of course I did. I was twelve now, after all. It must be awful, worrying about you and your family getting hit. Living in the countryside, we'd had a few air raid warnings, but no bombs, thank goodness. Those children needed somewhere safe to live.

Yet I wasn't keen to share my bedroom, my dolls, my bike. Selfish, I know – but it had always been just me.

Gran, who lived around the corner, came with Mum and me to help choose our evacuee. Lots of children were lined up in the school hall and Mum picked a girl called Peggy. Taller than me, with long, straggly fair hair, she stood there scowling, clutching her satchel and gas mask. Later, Mum said she felt sorry for her. "She looked lost."

Once home with us, though, she didn't act as if she was lost. For a start, she refused to eat the Spam sandwiches Gran made us for dinner. Then she pulled a face at my Charlie, curled up in a chair.

"Cats scratch!"

"My cat doesn't!" Glaring at her, I stroked my lovely bundle of black fur.

"Susie's nuts about him," smiled Gran. "When the sirens go, the family all come to my house to use my shelter. Susie always carts Charlie along! You'll get used to him."

Mum gave Peggy and me a look.

"You'll need to get used to each other, too. I'll see if we've any cheese left, Peggy."

Mum went into the kitchen. I stared after her. *Susie, there's a war on,* was the answer I always got when I moaned about powdered egg, or whatever. Yet this Peggy was about to get some of our precious cheese, which was rationed!

In the next few days, I tried hard to be friendly to Peggy, even sharing my sweet ration with her. Dad, who worked at the Power Station and was in the Home Guard, kept teasing her, saying he could cut off her hair and use it to tie up his runner beans in the garden. Peggy giggled, threatening to cut up his Daily Mirror if he did.

"Gives as good as she gets, that one!" Dad remarked.

"True. One of a big family, she's had to look out for herself," Mum answered.

I needn't have worried about sharing stuff. Peggy pooh-poohed my dolls, and looked horrified when I suggested a board game. As for reading, which I loved, that was "bloomin' boring!"

Then some of my coloured pencils went missing. I was sure Peggy had taken them – I'd chewed my green one on the end and hers looked the same. But she said the

pencils were a present from her auntie…
and Mum believed her.

One day, a couple of Mum's special
apples – her 'treats', she called them –
vanished from the dish on the sideboard
and I found Peggy munching one at school.
When I told Mum, she said maybe we
weren't feeding her enough!

Then Peggy borrowed Dad's box
camera to take pictures of Charlie
to send home… and afterwards the
camera wouldn't work. Dad just said
she'd never make a professional
photographer and spent ages
trying to mend it. Mum and Dad
were letting Peggy get away with
everything!

At school she struggled to
keep up and a gang of kids, led by
another evacuee – a boy called
David – laughed at her. Peggy
yelled back at them, then whined
to Mum.

"Ah, but David is billeted with
the Lawrences, a really strict
family," Mum answered. "He has
to toe the line with them, so he
probably takes it out on other
children."

Peggy just shrugged and
Mum changed the subject.

"Susie, you're good at
arithmetic – will you help
Peggy?"

I nodded. Well, I did
feel a bit sorry for her.
David and his pals could
get really nasty. Also, as
she was living with us,
I knew I could end up
getting bullied as well.

So, one night, while
Mum was working at
the Post Office and Dad
listening to the wireless
in the kitchen, I ➡

found paper and pens and sat down at the dining table.

"Shall we do some sums, then, Peggy?"

"No way!" she cried, carrying on dangling a toy mouse over Charlie's nose.

"But –"

"I said no! You're so bossy, Sue!"

With that, Peggy threw the mouse across the room and stormed upstairs. I felt angry… and annoyed that she kept calling me Sue, instead of Susie.

Trying to calm down, I opened *Black Beauty*, my very favourite book. Then I heard footsteps overhead. Golly, that was Mum and Dad's bedroom – and Dad was still in the kitchen. Peggy must be in there!

As I ran upstairs, a sweet, sickly smell wafted around me. Violets! Peggy had been at Mum's Ashes of Violets scent!

The bedroom door was open. Peggy stood there holding an empty scent bottle, her blue dress spattered with big damp patches, the lino around her feet shiny wet. The smell was overpowering, making my eyes water. Peggy smirked.

"I only meant to dab a bit on me!"

"Get a floor cloth, quick!" I yelled.

We mopped up as best we could and Peggy got changed, but the violet stench still lingered. At first, Dad told her off, then he joked, "I thought I'd died and gone to a flowery heaven!"

Mum would surely go mad this time!

But Peggy's apologies and tears worked wonders and Mum forgave her.

"She shouldn't have been in the bedroom, of course," Mum said, when we were on our own. "But it was an accident. Thanks for trying to help her with her sums, though, Susie." Mum gave me a hug. "Our Peggy can certainly be a difficult one!"

Things got worse. One very wet Saturday, when Mum was at work and Dad had been called out by the Home Guard, Peggy seemed extra bored.

"I'll get *Black Beauty*," I offered. "We can read it together."

"Don't bother," she answered quickly.

Ignoring her, I went up to fetch the book. Strange – it wasn't in its usual place on my bedside table. Alarmed, I looked everywhere, then ran downstairs.

"My book's missing –" I began.

"Ah, I tried readin' it," Peggy said.

"So, where is it?"

"In the garden, by the shed."

Oh, no! I tore outside in the pouring rain. My beloved *Black Beauty* lay there, all soggy and shrivelled. You could hardly read the title! Furious, I ran back in.

"Look at this!" I raved. "You wait until Mum comes home, Peggy! She's bound to give up on you now, what with this and all the other bad things you've done. They'll move you to some awful family, like they did David. Serves you right!"

I slammed the door and took the book up to my room. Hardly able to see for tears, I tried to smooth down the damp pages, but it was hopeless.

Later, an eerie sound echoed through the house. The air raid siren! I shuddered, all else forgotten as I ran downstairs.

"Peggy, we must go to Gran's –"

But Peggy wasn't there. I searched the house, even the lavvy down the garden. It had stopped raining; she must have gone out. Well, she knew to always make for Gran's in an air raid; she could be already on the way. Then I remembered Charlie; but he, too, was nowhere to be seen.

In the end, still fretting about both Peggy and the cat, I ran around to Gran's.

"Where's young Peggy?" she asked.

"She went out –"

"Well, she's sensible. She'll turn up."

I hated having to spend time in Gran's shelter. Damp and musty, it smelled like mouldy old rags and was always freezing, even in summer. Today, I thought about Peggy. I hated her for ruining my book, but supposing there were bombs for real and she got hit? I sat in the shelter on a rickety deckchair, biting my nails.

And what about Charlie? "Cats are canny, they look after themselves," Dad always said. He was probably right, but I still wished Charlie was here, safe with me.

After a bit, Gran was just saying she ought to go and look for Peggy, when Mum appeared at the entrance.

"I was on my way home when the siren went, so I made straight for here." Mum frowned. "Where's Peggy?"

"I dunno," I mumbled. "We had a row and she went out. She left *Black Beauty* out in the rain, Mum, and – "

Mum butted in.

"Peggy was upset, then?"

"Yes! I told her that, after doing so many bad things, you would definitely be sending her back and she'd end up with unfriendly people, like David did!"

Mum looked horrified and Gran gasped.

"You said what, Susie?" Mum said.

"That you'd send her away," I stuttered. I felt really bad. Had I thought about it, I'd have realised Mum would never do that, however awful Peggy was. "I'm sorry, Mum, I shouldn't have," I whispered.

"No, you shouldn't!" she said. "Peggy is stuck here with us – strangers – away from her family in London. Don't you think that might be the reason she keeps doing these 'bad things', as you call them? We can't be too hard on her." Then Mum put her arm around me. "Let's hope that in time she learns from my Susie, eh?"

I smiled back. I was the lucky one.

"Now, I must go and find –"

Mum stopped as someone else appeared at the entrance. I stared as Peggy staggered in, clutching something bulky which suddenly leapt out of her arms and darted across the shelter.

"Charlie!" I yelled happily. "I couldn't find you earlier –"

"I came in the back gate, knowin' you'd all be in here." A breathless Peggy sank down on the stone floor. "I was goin' to the library, Sue, to get you another *Black Beauty*. They're free, library books, see? Then the sirens went and I thought I'd better run back. I saw Charlie on a wall and picked him up, 'cos Gran said you always brought him."

Charlie was now purring loudly on my lap and I had a lump in my throat as I looked at Peggy. She wasn't so bad after all – bringing Charlie and trying to get me another book.

"Peggy – " I began. But she was looking imploringly at Mum.

"I don't want to go to someone else; please, Mrs Price! I'm sorry about the scent and the camera, and all that. And for spoiling your book, Sue. But –"

Mum went across and hugged her tight.

"You're not going anywhere, my love!"

"I'm sorry, too, Peggy," I said gruffly. "I shouldn't have said what I did."

Peggy smiled gratefully at me over Mum's shoulder just as the All Clear went.

"Now you two gals can be proper friends," Gran said.

Later, I came to realise this war had taught both Peggy and me lessons to last a lifetime. What's more, I even came to like being called Sue. Thanks to the evacuee. Ⓜ

....

MY INSPIRATION

I am inspired to write when I read and admire classic short story writers such as Katherine Mansfield and William Trevor. I learn so much from them, especially about characterisation and construction.

Slippery Slope

A chalet maid's workload can snowball when she's left to cope alone… how can she get back on piste?

By Jan Snook

Sarah turned away from the computer, where she was unenthusiastically looking at jobs, and answered her mobile.

It was her friend Charlotte, who was in the French Alps for the skiing season, working as a chalet girl in a chalet her parents owned.

"You sound down. Is everything OK?" Charlotte asked.

"I'm looking at jobs," Sarah said, unable to bring herself to tell Charlotte about Mike, her ex-boyfriend. And ex-boss. At ex-work.

"That's why I'm ringing. The other chalet girl's just walked out! I mean, couldn't she have just stuck it out for another month? So how do you fancy

The invitation, Sarah thought as she boarded the plane the next day, couldn't have come at a better time. A few weeks as a chalet girl with Charlotte was just what she needed.

It would be a laugh, Charlotte said. A spot of housekeeping in the morning, and quickly whipping up something for the guests' evening meal, and that was it. Oh, and something for tea. The whole of the rest of the day to enjoy the blue skies, sparkling snow and skiing. Then there would be cosy evenings in front of a log fire, sipping mulled wine, and chatting merrily to a hunky ski instructor… it sounded idyllic. And she'd be far away from Mike.

The chalet was beautiful, and the eleven guests seemed friendly enough. Charlotte had already prepared that night's meal and all Sarah had to do was help serve it.

The ski instructor was called Brian, far from irresistible and very grumpy

being a chalet girl? A month's skiing, with a bit of work on the side? We need you! Please say yes!"

"Well I can't actually ski…"

"Mum says she'll throw some lessons in – that's how desperate we are!"

There was a pause.

"Will Mike be OK with that?"

Another pause.

"Actually, Mike's dumped me."

"Dumped you? But why?" Charlotte shrieked. "So there's nothing to stop you coming to France, is there!"

"Oh, and by the way, I've told them you're a very experienced chalet girl. And I sort of implied that you're an expert skier as well…"

The next morning Sarah woke up to brilliant sunshine and postcard views of mountains. She hurried down to the kitchen where Charlotte was busy with breakfast.

"It's such a relief to have you here," Charlotte said gratefully. "I had to manage for two whole days on my own, and it was absolute murder!"

Once the guests appeared downstairs

there was no time to waste. Breakfast was a whirlwind, with the guests eager to get out on the slopes as fast as possible. At last, all but one of them had gone.

"You still here then, Jack?" Charlotte said, artificially bright. "You can still catch up with your friends if you hurry."

Jack looked at his watch. "I'll see them at lunch. They're all much better skiers than I am, so I think I'll just have some more coffee and then be on my way."

"Great," Charlotte said, looking relieved. Sarah poured him another cup and was rewarded with a ravishing smile.

After he'd gone, Charlotte and Sarah cleared the breakfast, made the beds and tidied the chalet. Charlotte was anxious to get on to the slopes too, and said she'd make some scones for tea after lunch.

"They always come back ravenous," she said, but Sarah was hardly listening. Jack's smile was still filling her brain.

"I haven't managed to sort out who's with whom," she said, trying to sound as if it was just a casual question.

Charlotte, however, laughed.

"If you mean who Jack's here with," she said, "he's a friend of Hugo and Jane's." She raised an eyebrow. "You could do worse."

"Oh no," Sarah said firmly, "I've had it with men. Unless my ski instructor is irresistible, of course!"

The ski instructor was, however, far from irresistible. A tanned fit young Frenchman he was not. Despite his job he was burly, fiftyish, called Brian and came from the Midlands. He was also extremely grumpy.

"The rest of the class have already had three lessons. And I've got to start all over again with you…"

This was done with such a bad grace (and Sarah was so sore from her numerous falls) that at the end of the lesson – instead of practising, as instructed – she went back to the chalet. The chalet was empty, and Sarah thought she should start on the scones, but it was still early, so instead she lay in a hot bath. It was heaven.

There were noises from downstairs when she eventually surfaced. Good. Charlotte must be back.

But it wasn't Charlotte. It was Jack. He had already put the kettle on. ➝

"Anything for tea?" he asked.

"I didn't think you'd be back yet," Sarah said, flustered. "Where's Charlotte?"

"Haven't seen her, sorry." He was gazing at her with undisguised interest.

Sarah looked at her watch. She'd spent far longer in the bath than she'd realised. She hurriedly started weighing ingredients and made the fastest thing she knew – cinnamon cookies.

Jack sat at the kitchen table, asking her about herself (while she worried about the dinner) until the other guests arrived, tired and hungry. At last, fortified by tea and cookies, they all disappeared upstairs, and Sarah was able to get on.

But where was Charlotte?

And then her mobile rang.

"Charlotte. At last!"

But a heavily accented voice replied.

Sarah listened in horror: Charlotte had had a skiing accident and been flown to a hospital miles away. Sarah was on her own.

The guests, who had gobbled up cookies appreciatively earlier, stared at their simple dinner in consternation, and there were muttered rumblings about chalet girls who thoughtlessly broke their legs ("everyone knows skiing's risky…"), leaving one incompetent girl in their place. Sarah was hugely grateful to Jack – who defended her valiantly – but it wasn't a good start.

The next day she got up at dawn, wondering when Charlotte's mother would send in reinforcements, and managed to get everything done before her ski class, but she wondered why she'd bothered.

"You're not trying!" Brian shouted at her, and the class tutted. She was holding them back.

By day four she was dead on her feet. No help had arrived, and she went unwillingly to her class. If she fell just one more time (and she would) she'd have to give up. Why had Charlotte said it was easy?

She hurried back to the chalet, conscious that she hadn't yet finished clearing up the breakfast things. She went straight into the kitchen and stopped dead.

The breakfast dishes were nowhere in sight. Jack, wearing her apron, was carefully lifting a tray of shortbread out of the oven.

"Hope you don't mind," he said diffidently, "I was getting withdrawal symptoms. From the kitchen," he said, seeing her puzzled look. "I've just bought a small – tiny – restaurant in the West Country, so I'm practising. On your guests," he added sheepishly. "This was for today, wasn't it?" He was holding up her menu plan, written last night. Or rather, at about two in the morning.

Sarah gazed around. Through the oven door she could see (and smell) a delicious casserole, and under it was a traditional French apple flan. On the worktop nearby was what looked like her salmon mousse.

"And don't worry, I kept faithfully to your recipes," he continued – but then he stopped.

Sarah could feel her bottom lip wobbling.

"Whatever's the matter? Oh sweetheart, please don't cry."

"But you're a guest," she gulped. "This is my job and everything's going wrong!" Tears splashed down her cheeks. "There were supposed to be two of us and I hardly speak French and now Charlotte's broken her leg and…"

"And your ski classes aren't going well," Jack said, dabbing at her tears with a tea towel.

"How do you know?"

"Your bruises," Jack said, smiling and indicating the purple blotches on Charlotte's arms.

"I'm black and blue all over," she said.

"So not quite the Olympic skier Charlotte made you out to be?"

"She wanted me to sound like an experienced chalet girl," Sarah admitted.

"And you're not?"

Sarah shook her head. All this sympathy was making her feel tearful again.

"Well I think you've done wonders," Jack said seriously. "Have some tea. And some shortbread. You may not have been a chalet girl before, but you're a brilliant cook. I'd employ you any time." Then he frowned. "But no one could manage this all on their own. There's far too much to do."

The next day Sarah got up early to make breakfast only to find Jack already in the kitchen, hard at work.

She couldn't let him carry on helping. He was missing hours of skiing, and she knew keen skiers looked forward to their (wildly expensive) week on the slopes all year.

If she dropped her own skiing lessons she'd have time to get everything done. She cleared the breakfast and checked her menu for the evening. She'd make her signature lime and blueberry cake. That might redeem her reputation.

She ran upstairs as soon as it was in the oven. The first bedroom she went into was extraordinarily neat and tidy, and the bed was made. She looked more closely. There were vacuum cleaner marks on the carpet. Then she heard a sound in the room next door. But that was Jane and Hugo's room, and she'd watched them leave an hour ago. She crept into the corridor and quietly opened the door. Jack was kneeling

at the vacuum. "Something's caught in the brushes," he said, looking up.

"I thought you'd gone out!" she shouted. "What are you doing? You're supposed to be out on the slopes whizzing down! You're not supposed to be doing my job for me!"

"But you're exhausted," he said simply. "And I only came because Hugo asked me to. I've discovered I hate skiing."

"What?"

"Almost as much as you do, I imagine. I saw you yesterday when I went to tell Brian I was quitting. If you think your bruises are bad, you should see mine! Anyway, we must get on or you'll miss your own class."

"I'm not going. You're right, I loathe it. So I've got all day to do my job, and you've got all day to go out and do… whatever it is non-skiers do in ski resorts."

Jack abandoned the vacuum and stood up. Before Sarah knew what he was doing he'd put his arms round her.

"What I want to do is spend time with you," he said gently. "Cooking or cleaning or making the beds, whatever's needed. And then I want to spend time with you having fun. We could start," he said, "by going for a sleigh ride. I'd like to see Alpine scenery going past at ten miles an hour, not sixty. And I prefer the sound of tinkling sleigh bells to Brian yelling at me. We've tried skiing – time we tried a bit of après-ski instead."

Then he kissed her… Ⓜ

MY INSPIRATION

I once spent three months working in a restaurant in a French ski resort, which inspired this story. Very fortunately it was in the summer: the idea of hurtling down mountains at speed terrifies me!

Scottish Shortbread

Ingredients
(Serves 8)

- ◆ **160g plain flour**
- ◆ **3tbsp ground rice flour**
- ◆ **125g butter, at room temperature, cut into pieces**
- ◆ **50g caster sugar, plus extra for sprinkling**

230 Calories per serving

1 Preheat the oven to 180°C/Fan 160°C/Gas 4. Sift the flours into a bowl. Cream the butter and sugar together. Gradually knead the flours into the creamed mixture to form a smooth dough.

2 On a lightly floured surface, roll the dough into an 18cm round, then place in a lightly floured shortbread mould, or plain flan ring. Turn out of the mould on to a baking sheet.

3 If using a flan ring, transfer the shortbread to the baking sheet and remove the ring. Prick well with a fork. Pinch up the edges and mark into 8 segments, if wished.

4 Bake for 20min then reduce the oven to 170°C/Fan 150°C/Gas 3 and cook for a further 10-15min, or until pale golden. Leave for 10min then transfer to a wire rack to cool. Dredge with a little caster sugar. Cool, then store in an airtight container until served.

A Tiny Christmas Miracle

Even if Viv succeeds in dragging her resentful teenager to the Nativity play, what will happen then?…

By Sheila Blackburn

"Do I have to?"

Mel's lovely face was distorted with anger and revulsion. Again.

Viv stood in the doorway and sighed. She felt frustrated too – with her funny, pretty daughter who had turned into this teenage monster.

"It's just a Primary School Nativity play," she said and knew she was not saving what little was left of her patience.

"Exactly – who wants to go to a kids' play, anyway?" Mel sighed, long and loud.

There was a pause as Viv wondered if it would be easier to just take the baby and go. But there was something else to be considered here. Something more than all the extra work and Christmas preparations that were expected and never shared…

"Your sister is an angel –"

"Don't we know it!"

"She's learned all her words and she looks so good in her costume."

"And?"

Viv perched on the arm of a chair, trying not to be confrontational.

"And I know it will mean such a lot to her if you come to this afternoon's performance."

Mel regarded her mother with a look that said, *Neat move.* She adored her little sister. Always had, from the moment Katie was born and placed on her knee in a lacy shawl. Being the big sister was a role she stepped into so easily; helping with feeds and baths, learning to change a nappy and dress the infant like one of her dolls, to play with her, follow her when she crawled, hold her hand when she took her first steps.

Mum, Dad and two daughters. The perfect family. But now there was Jack. The baby. New born…

If Viv had thought for a nanosecond that Mel would welcome another baby, she couldn't have been more wrong.

"Gross!" Mel had greeted the news of the pregnancy with horror. Viv could only imagine the comments flying around on social media: two oldies getting it together. Having a baby at their age. She knew that her older daughter had to join in with the shocked teenage reactions to save face. But she had been so distressed to find that those first impressions never changed. As the bump grew, so Mel distanced herself from the plans and excitement. This time, it was six-year-old Katie who listened for the heartbeat, put her hand on her Mum's tummy to feel ➤

ILLUSTRATIONS: SHUTTERSTOCK, ISTOCKPHOTO

the baby kicking, helped sort the nursery.

"It's a boy!" Katie yelled at her big sister.

Mel lay on her bed and turned away to face the wall. "Yeah. Whatever."

"Now I'm a big sister too!"

"Good luck with that. It's no big deal," Mel muttered and left her little sister to the baby duties.

In the two weeks since the house had been swamped with blue teddies to vie with so much pink and sparkle, not once had Mel looked into the cot, let alone held the new arrival. Wisely, Viv said nothing.

"What is her problem?" Rick was ever the doting father, now looking forward to football in the garden and joking about buying his son a first pint.

"She is a mass of muddled hormones – and a slave to social media and being on trend," Viv told him. "It's just not cool to have this happen right now."

"Is that right?" Rick shook his head, baffled by this logic. "Women! Eh, son?"

Viv flicked him with a cushion then, but now she felt far less confident.

Perched on the chair arm, she wished

By the time they reached the school gates, Viv knew they were on the last minute. A kindly pupil held the door open and she pushed the pram through the entrance hall that was practically filled with a sweet-smelling Christmas tree. She sensed Mel, several paces behind.

"I'm so sorry. No seats left – but you can stand here at the back."

This at the hall door from one of the staff – Miss Briggs – whom Viv recognised as a teacher of the class above Katie.

"You can leave the pram right by the door, so you'll be able to see it – and if baby cries…"

"Thank you," Viv whispered and felt Mel beside her, awkward and morose.

"We just need to leave this gap for the choir to walk through." Miss Briggs was happily in charge of front of house. She smiled warmly and Viv noticed the tinsel in her hair. There was something very happy about her; even Mel managed the flicker of a passing smile under that welcoming gaze.

Viv sighed softly and allowed herself

"Suppose you'll have to bring him too?" Mel glared at the pram in the hall

she could find the words to reach her daughter, but all she could think about was the play – and what sort of Christmas they were facing if this atmosphere continued.

"So – will you come with me?" she asked, simply and to the point.

"Suppose you'll have to bring him, too?" Mel glared at the pram that stood ready in the hallway.

Resisting the urge to say that Jack could hardly stay home and look after himself, Viv stood up. She put on her coat and sensed that Mel would follow. No need for words, for thanks or anything else. A small victory. Nothing more.

to relax. Within moments, a line of wide-eyed children filed past to take their places either side of the stage, lit by two more impressive trees. Still smiling, Miss Briggs dimmed the hall lights and the annual story began.

Two narrators paved the way to Nazareth and it was there that Katie appeared, trying not to trip up the steps in her long dress, her hair still freshly combed and her wings only slightly askew. Viv smiled proudly, recalling how Mel had once appeared on this stage as the innkeeper's wife, her hair in rollers and wearing a full length nightdress and slippers. Now, she glanced sideways and was rewarded by Mel's steady gaze as she quietly mouthed her sister's words in the shadows. It was more than she had dared to hope for.

There followed much donkey clip-clopping round the hall to Bethlehem and that moment where the innkeeper's mother holds her breath in case the words get changed and room is found in the Inn after two millennia. Then, off to the stable; much lifting and positioning of the manger and hay bales – and Miss Briggs flitting about in a state of Nativity panic.

"It appears the baby Jesus doll has gone missing!" This from Rick who had now joined his wife at the back of the hall. Even Mel was interested.

"How do you know?"

"I took a wrong turn somewhere and got caught up in the search – apparently, the doll was on loan from an infant who changed her mind and took it home…"

Viv smiled. "They probably have more in the Reception class?"

"All gone to be washed so they can dry over the holidays," Rick was a font of information. "Miss Briggs is swaddling some other object as we speak."

Indeed, Viv was aware of Miss Briggs heading backstage, bearing a swaddled bundle which, in due course, Angel Katie carried on and placed in the manger.

It was at that precise moment that baby Jack began to cry. Viv moved quickly to the pram and lifted him out, pacing the entrance hall to soothe him.

Miss Briggs appeared. "You saved the day!" she exclaimed, her eyes bright with tears. "My DIY baby looked like a swaddled sausage, but then your little one cried as we sang *Away In A Manger*… so atmospheric … hardly a dry eye in the house." With that, she was gone.

Rick gave a thumbs-up. Viv cradled her son and crept back into the hall between her husband and older daughter. They watched with pride as the shepherds were visited by Katie and her throng of angels, shuffling into line and off again.

Baby Jack slept on as the shepherds circled the hall on their way to the stable, only to find one had forgotten the gift of a lamb (Miss Briggs almost threw it onto the stage from the wings)… as the Kings pointed a decidedly wobbly star in the east, then made their way round the hall to Herod and on to the Bethlehem stable… as Katie visited them in their dreams with warnings about their journey home… as she instructed Joseph to flee to Egypt…

Then it was over and the choir stood to sing one last song as the entire cast assembled on stage, around the manger, where Mary sat on a bale of straw.

Viv loved it all. Had done through all the years since Mel was an infant. Maybe it was the warmth in the hall, the emotions so soon after giving birth, hormones… whatever. Suddenly, her eyes filled with tears and she felt herself swaying.

To her left, Rick didn't notice. It ➙

was Mel, standing slightly behind her, who reached forward and took the baby from her, so carefully, as she had done with Katie, years before.

"Thank you."

The words were hardly out of her mouth before she realised that Mel was walking away… walking calmly and deliberately down the centre of the hall, between the rows of audience chairs, towards the stage as cameras clicked and families waved at their children. The choir filed out and Miss Briggs ushered most of the cast off the stage, calmly and quietly. It was over. And yet something else had just begun.

Mel reached out and took the baby from Mary's knee, handed him to her mother and nodded very slightly. Then she went back down the steps to stand by Viv and at that moment, they understood each other.

There was a collective holding of breath as she climbed the two steps to the stage

towards the stage. The choir finished the song as Mel reached the front. There was a collective holding of breath as she climbed the two steps up and very gently laid her baby brother on Mary's knee.

He nestled there safely, small and sleeping, as Mel knelt beside him, head bent yet watchful.

The silence in the school hall was deep and moving. Then a gentle clapping began and the entire room was filled with something very special.

At the back, Miss Briggs was still; she sniffed very slightly. Viv watched as Katie the angel moved to stand beside her big sister and baby brother.

Rick's hand on her arm was gently urging her to move.

"She knows what she's doing." Viv smiled up at him. "She needed to do this."

The head teacher was standing in front of the stage, visibly moved, telling the audience she was lost for words, in spite of preparing a speech. Viv made her way

Close and strong again. Inseparable.

Rick helped Katie off the stage, put an arm round her shoulders and looked at his older daughter with a new fondness.

"Thank you for looking after the baby."

Viv spoke gently to the girl who played Mary, whose parents were looking on proudly. The child smiled.

"Thank you for letting me hold him," she said. "I like him – he's special."

"Yes. He is."

Mel's words were all Viv needed this Christmas. She felt her family close round her. It felt so very comforting.

Togetherness. Understanding. A tiny Christmas miracle. Ⓜ

. . . .

MY INSPIRATION

I am a retired primary teacher and writer of children's reading books, and now love writing for adults. My inspiration? I'm fascinated by everyday life – and am seldom short of material!

Each Week For You To Enjoy

My Weekly

Amazing Cookery

Favourite Celebrities

Fabulous Fiction

Up-to-date Health News

PLUS

◆ **Puzzles** ◆ **Fashion** ◆ **Beauty** ◆ **Real Life**

Your Feel Good Read

You'll Love It!
On Sale Every Tuesday